BTEC Level 3 National Study Skills Guide in Health and Social Care

Welcome to your Study Skills Guide! You can make it your own – start by adding your personal and course details below...

Learner's name: _____

BTEC course title: _____

Date started: _____

Mandatory units:

_____

_____

_____

Optional units:

_____

_____

_____

_____

Centre name: _____

Centre address:

_____

_____

_____

Tutor's name: _____

Published by Pearson Education Limited, a company incorporated in England and Wales, having its registered office at Edinburgh Gate, Harlow, Essex, CM20 2JE. Registered company number: 872828

Edexcel is a registered trademark of Edexcel Limited

Text © Pearson Education Limited 2010

First published 2010

17

17

British Library Cataloguing in Publication Data

A catalogue record for this book is available from the British Library

ISBN 978 1 84690 558 2

Typeset and edited by Sparks Publishing Services Ltd
Cover design by Visual Philosophy, created by eMC Design
Cover photo/illustration © Plainpicture: Fstop
Printed in Great Britain by Ashford Colour Press Ltd

Acknowledgements
The publisher would like to thank the following for their kind permission to reproduce their photographs:

Alamy Images: Angela Hampton Picture Library 20, Christa Stadtler / Photofusion Picture Library 76, Claudia Wiens 58; **Corbis:** 68, Gabe Palmer 11; **iStockphoto:** Chris Schmidt 33; **Pearson Education Ltd:** Steve Shott 28, Ian Wedgewood 51

Cover images: *Front:* **Plainpicture Ltd:** Andreas Schlegel / fStop

All other images © Pearson Education

Every effort has been made to trace the copyright holders and we apologise in advance for any unintentional omissions. We would be pleased to insert the appropriate acknowledgement in any subsequent edition of this publication.

Websites
Go to www.peasonhotlinks.co.uk to gain access to the relevant website links and information on how they can aid your studies. When you access the site, search for either the title BTEC Level 3 National Study Skills Guide in Health and Social Care or ISBN 9781846905582.

Disclaimer
This material has been published on behalf of Edexcel and offers high-quality support for the delivery of Edexcel qualifications.

This does not mean that the material is essential to achieve any Edexcel qualification, nor does it mean that it is the only suitable material available to support any Edexcel qualification. Edexcel material will not be used verbatim in setting any Edexcel examination or assessment. Any resource lists produced by Edexcel shall include this and other appropriate resources.

Copies of official specifications for all Edexcel qualifications may be found on the Edexcel website: www.edexcel.com

Contents

Popular progression pathways

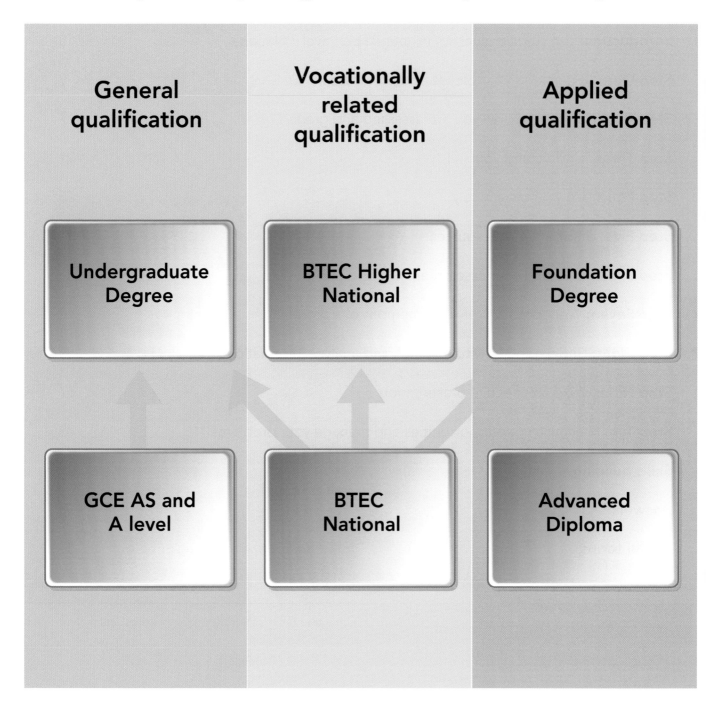

Ten steps to success in your BTEC Level 3 National

This Study Skills Guide has been written to help you achieve the best result possible on your BTEC Level 3 National course. At the start of a new course you may feel both quite excited but also a little apprehensive. Taking a BTEC Level 3 National qualification has many benefits and is a major stepping stone towards your future career. Using this Study Skills Guide will help you get the most out of your course from the start.

> ## TOP TIP
>
> Use this Study Skills Guide at your own pace. Dip in to find what you need. Look back at it whenever you have a problem or query.

During **induction** sessions at the start of your course, your tutor will explain important information, but it can be difficult to remember everything and that's when you'll find this Study Skills Guide invaluable. Look at it whenever you want to check anything related to your course. It provides all the essential facts you need and has a Useful terms section to explain specialist terms, words and phrases, including some that you will see highlighted in this book in bold type.

This Study Skills Guide covers the skills you'll need to do well in your course – such as managing your time, researching and analysing information and preparing a presentation.

- Use the **Top tips** to make your life easier.
- Use the **Key points** to help you to stay focused on the essentials.
- Use the **Action points** to check what you need to know or do now.
- Use the **Case studies** to relate information to your chosen sector and vocational area.
- Try out the **Activities** to test your knowledge and skills.
- Use the **Useful terms** section to check the meaning of specialist terms.

This Study Skills Guide has been designed to work alongside the Edexcel Student Textbook for BTEC Level 3 National Health and Social Care (Edexcel, 2010). This Student Book includes the main knowledge you'll need, with tips from BTEC experts, Edexcel assignment tips, assessment activities and up-to-date case studies from industry experts, plus handy references to your Study Skills Guide.

This Study Skills Guide is divided into ten steps, each relating to a key aspect of your studies, from understanding assessment to time management to maximising opportunities. Concentrate on getting things right one step at a time. Thousands of learners have achieved BTEC Level 3 National qualifications and are now studying for a degree, or building a successful career at work. Using this Study Skills Guide, and believing in your own abilities, will help you achieve your future goals, too.

Introduction to health and social care

Health and Social Care courses offer learners the opportunity to study a broad selection of health-related topics. They can be used to help you enter many different vocational settings. Once you have completed your studies, and have reached the age of 18, you will be able to apply for a wide variety of jobs.

These may include:

- working in children's nurseries
- working in schools
- working in residential and nursing homes for elderly people or adults with learning difficulties
- being social service key workers
- being support workers in hospitals.

Through careful selection of units, you should be able to gain work experience in a wide variety of care settings, helping you to decide on possible future career pathways.

While completing your course you can expect to learn through a variety of interesting and fun methods, allowing you the chance to explore concepts in a safe and supportive environment. You may be taught through the use of videos, DVDs and interactive technology as well as more traditional classroom-based studies. You may also hear from guest speakers and visit care settings – these are very valuable tools in adding relevant health-related material to your experience.

All Level 3 BTEC National Health and Social Care courses are comprised of mandatory and specialist units. Mandatory units give learners the opportunity to develop the fundamental skills necessary to be an effective carer in any health and care setting. You will be taught how to develop appropriate communication skills to use with service users and health care professionals. Emphasis is placed on developing empathy and understanding the needs of interpersonal relationships in care settings.

You must also develop an understanding of the importance of equality and diversity in society. You will be encouraged to explore the concepts of acceptance and tolerance, as well as being taught to recognise and then address personal and societal prejudices. Learners will also need to explore the place of health and safety legislation in care settings to ensure that clients are cared for in a safe environment.

Personal professional development plays an important role within academic study, particularly in Health and Social Care. Learners are required to explore their own development over the two years of study, considering personal learning styles and theories of reflection. Alongside 150 hours of work experience in care settings, you will begin to explore your own developmental needs, ultimately making you a better practitioner.

BTEC National courses are awarded UCAS points, which can be used to apply for university courses. You may consider university courses such as:

- nursing adults or children with physical, mental or learning difficulties
- primary school teaching
- sociology and psychology
- paramedic training
- medical technician training
- midwifery.

Whatever the route or eventual outcome, Level 3 BTEC National Health and Social Care students can be assured of a varied and interesting programme of study, leading to a satisfying and worthwhile career where caring for others is the main focus.

Skills for your sector

Health and Social Care students have the opportunity to develop a wealth of skills that will help them in their studies and in the workplace. You have the dual task of developing skills to aid your course studies as well as developing the skills to work within the health and social care sector. You will need an inquisitive mind and the desire to continue learning throughout your working life. The healthcare sector is constantly changing and evolving to incorporate new methods of care and new medical discoveries.

Vocational skills

Learners on Health and Social Care courses undoubtedly have a real desire to help people, but this is not enough on its own to let you become an effective carer. Beyond having the desire to help and care for someone, you need to be professional and able to distance yourself from difficult and sometimes distressing emotions.

This may seem cold and cruel, but being a good carer is also about being able to make decisions based on knowledge and information, while not being persuaded or influenced by personal beliefs. Learners must understand the need to act professionally and conduct themselves in a professional manner, abiding by codes of conduct and ethics that govern healthcare professionals, irrespective of their own personal emotions and beliefs. At the same time, you must be able to empathise with clients and understand the situation they find themselves in.

Communication skills

Effective communication is very important in health and social care. With good communication skills, learners will be able to help support service users in many different care settings. You will need to develop many new skills tailored to the workplaces you may find yourself in. These may be anything from helping children put on a play to holding the hand of a dying patient. A positive attitude and pleasant demeanour are vital in building rapport and establishing a level of mutual trust with clients, their families and other health professionals.

Effective communication involves learning a fine balance between when to listen and when to talk. It is a skill only developed with practice. Interpersonal communication skills include such things as having a good attitude to work, interacting with others, working well with people from different cultures and backgrounds, being able to set and achieve goals, having good common sense, solving problems, and making good and quick decisions.

Practical skills

Every job within health and social care will have its own set of practical skills that learners will need to develop in order to effectively fulfil their role. For example, a midwife will learn how to care for pregnant women and ultimately how to deliver a baby. An oncology nurse will learn how to care for terminally ill clients and their families. Practical skills are usually learned in the workplace or in specially designed learning environments that simulate the workplace.

BTEC National Health and Social Care learners have the unique opportunity to develop practical skills while on their work placements. Skills as simple as being able to make a bed properly will ensure that clients don't develop pressure sores and are able to sleep well, which will ultimately help speed up their recovery. Never underestimate the value placed on learners

in work placements. Learners are often in the unique position to be able to talk to clients at length, sometimes resulting in them finding out about a problem that has been missed by busy medical staff. Practical skills form the basis of any specialised healthcare profession, but they take time to develop and practice.

Study skills

To become an effective learner and achieve the best from your course, you will need to become an independent thinker and develop strategies to manage your time effectively, ensuring that you are able to meet assignment deadlines.

Listening

One of the most important study skills that learners require to study effectively is that of listening. Since most information is delivered through taught sessions, DVDs, videos and tutorials, it is imperative that you learn to listen. When you listen properly, you are not only hearing what is being said but also processing what it means. Learners need to pay attention to their teachers – not only to the words they speak but also to the thoughts and messages they convey. You need to identify the main idea or concept being addressed. This involves listening for explanations, descriptions and clarifications – not just hearing words but listening to their meaning.

You will need to develop skills in note taking, learning to jot down what is important and not trying to record everything that is being said. It's important to be selective in your choice of material, recording what is relevant to the topic being explored. Learners who find listening difficult often find it hard to concentrate as well. Try to remove all distracting thoughts, temporarily forgetting about any personal problems and home life, so you can focus on your studies.

Preparing written work

All units on Level 3 BTEC National in Health and Social Care courses require students to submit coursework in the form of assignments. Make sure that you involve your teachers when planning assignments, asking for help and advice where necessary. If you are given a choice of topics, choose something that interests you, as this will ensure that you put in the effort necessary to get a good grade. You may be disappointed with the results of your first assignments but this is often due to lack of preparation, and tutors will provide support to help you do better in future.

Good assignment presentation is essential to achieve a good grade. Teaching staff will guide learners on how they should present their coursework. This may include a front cover, contents list, introduction, evaluation and reference list. Some assignments may even be submitted as videos and tape recording. In this case students will need to develop the skills necessary to produce their work in the desired format.

When preparing to submit work, following these guidelines may be helpful.

- The material selected is relevant.
- Information is gathered from a variety of sources.
- Information is accurate and from a suitable source.
- Any images included are relevant and support the written work.
- Written work is presented in a clear and legible manner.
- Spelling, punctuation and grammar have been checked.

Using research

Using relevant research is very important to support ideas and discussion points. It is a skill you will need to develop to succeed in higher education. You can gather information from primary resources, such as conducting interviews, surveys and questionnaires. Once the information is collected, you will need to analyse the findings and decide which information is relevant to the assignment. All too often pieces of research

are added to assignments for no good reason. Learners need to develop the skills necessary to be selective with the information they choose to use in an assignment.

The Internet, books, newspapers, magazines and statistics offer important secondary sources, which you can reference within your assignments. Learners need to develop the skills necessary to reference the information they choose to add to their work. Information should be referenced in the text and listed as a supplementary bibliography. Teachers will guide learners in the use of appropriate reference methods.

Working in a team

As well as working independently, you will get the opportunity to work in small groups or as part of a team, both in your centres and during work experience. Learners need to develop the skills necessary to communicate one to one and in group settings, as effective communication is very important in health and social care environments. When working in a team, learners must be able to do the following.

- Give and receive feedback from peers and other team members.
- Acknowledge and appreciate others' skills, experiences and contributions.
- Listen to and acknowledge the feelings and concerns of others.
- State personal opinions even if the team may not agree with them.
- Listen patiently.
- Talk in a non-threatening manner.
- Support group decisions even if you don't agree with them.
- Share information.
- Check that others understand your meaning.
- Negotiate to achieve a desired outcome.

Learners need to be able to prove to employers that they have the skills to work independently and within a team.

Step One: Understand your course and how it works

Case study: Where could the BTEC National in Health and Social Care take you?

Arianne is 18 years old. She is in the final year of a BTEC National Diploma in Health and Social Care, which she is studying at a college of Further Education. She has applied to university to do a degree in general nursing. She is very excited as she has her university interview next week. Unfortunately, at the weekend she falls off her moped, badly cutting her face and breaking her leg. She needs to spend a long time in hospital as her leg needs major surgery. Arianne is very anxious that she won't be able to complete her BTEC National Diploma, which may affect her getting into university.

Arianne's tutor is able to reassure her that she will be able to become a general nurse as she has already completed enough units to enter university at diploma level. As Arianne has completed the 8 core units and 4 specialists units of her BTEC National programme, she has the units necessary to complete the BTEC National Certificate in Health and Social Care, which may get her into university to do a diploma in nursing.

Reflection point

Think about how you might continue your studies if faced with a similar situation.

Activity: Your future options

At the beginning of a new course it is helpful to think about what options may be available to you for your career pathway in health and social care. All assignments and work experience on the programme contribute to your final grade and knowing what you are aiming for will help keep you motivated.

Using a list to explore different ideas is a way for you to start to consider the range of options available to you and what you will need to follow each career pathway.

For example, if you wish to work in the NHS, you could explore the different routes to becoming a social worker.

You will find the Internet a useful source of information. A good starting point is the website of NHS Jobs.

Use the space on the following page to list the different routes you can explore.

BTEC BTEC's own resources

All BTEC Level 3 National qualifications are **vocational** or **work-related**. This means that you gain specific knowledge and understanding relevant to your chosen area. It gives you several advantages when you start work.

For example, you will already know quite a lot about your chosen area, which will help you settle down more quickly. If you are already employed, you become more valuable to your employer.

Your BTEC course will prepare you for the work you want to do.

There are four types of BTEC Level 3 National qualification: Certificates, Subsidiary Diplomas, Diplomas and Extended Diplomas

	Certificate	Subsidiary Diploma	Diploma	Extended Diploma
Credit	30	60	120	180
Equivalence	1 AS-level	1 A-level	2 A-levels	3 A-levels

These qualifications are often described as **nested**. This means that they fit inside each other (rather like Russian dolls) because the same units are common to each qualification – so you can progress from one to another easily by completing more units.

TOP TIP

The structure of BTEC Level 3 National qualifications means it's easy to progress from one type to another and gain more credits, as well as specialise in particular areas that interest you.

- Every BTEC Level 3 National qualification has a set number of **mandatory units** that all learners must complete.
- All BTEC Level 3 National qualifications include **optional units** that enable you to study particular areas in more depth.
- Some BTEC Level 3 National qualifications have **specialist pathways**, which may have additional mandatory units. These specialist pathways allow you to follow your career aims more precisely. For example, if you are studying to become an IT practitioner, you can choose between pathways in Software Development, Networking, Systems Support or IT and Business.

- On all BTEC courses you are expected to be responsible for your own learning. Obviously your tutor will give you help and guidance when necessary but you also need to be 'self-starting' and able to use your own initiative. Ideally, you can also assess how well you are doing and make improvements when necessary.

- BTEC Level 3 National grades convert to UCAS points, just like A-levels, but the way you are assessed and graded on a BTEC course is different, as you will see in the next section.

Key points

- You can study part-time or full-time for your BTEC Level 3 National.

- You can do a Certificate, Subsidiary Diploma, Diploma, or Extended Diploma, and progress easily from one to the other.

- You will study both mandatory units and optional units on your course.

- When you have completed your BTEC course you can get a job (or **apprenticeship**), use your qualification to develop your career and/or continue studying to degree level.

- On all BTEC Level 3 National courses, the majority of your learning is practical and vocationally focused to develop the skills you need for your chosen career.

Using the Edexcel website to find out about your course

- You can check all the details about your BTEC Level 3 National course on the Edexcel website – go to www.edexcel.com

- Enter the title of your BTEC Level 3 National qualification in the qualifications finder.

- Now find the specification in the list of documents. This is a long document so don't try to print it. Instead, look at the information on the units you will be studying to see the main topics you will cover.

- Then save the document or bookmark the page so that you can easily refer to it again if you need to.

Action points

1 By discussing with your tutor and by exploring the Edexcel website, find out the key information about your course and use it to complete the 'Important Information' form on the next page. You can refer to this form at any time to refresh your memory about any part of your studies.

a) Check whether you are studying for a BTEC Level 3 Certificate, Subsidiary Diploma, Diploma, or Extended Diploma and the number of units you will be studying.

b) Find out the titles of the mandatory units you will be studying.

c) Find out the titles of the optional units and identify the ones offered at your centre.

d) Check the length of your course, and when you will be studying each unit.

e) Identify the optional units you will be taking.

On some National courses you will do this at the start, while on others you may make your final decision later.

f) Find out other relevant information about your BTEC Level 3 National qualification. Your centre may have already given you details about the structure.

g) Ask your tutor to help you to complete point 10 on the form. Depending on your course, you may be developing specific additional or personal skills – such as personal, learning and thinking skills (PLTS) and functional skills – or spending time on work experience, going on visits or doing other activities linked to your subject area.

h) Talk to your tutor about point 12 on the form as your sources of information will depend on the careers guidance and information at your centre. You may find it useful to exchange ideas with other members of your class.

	IMPORTANT INFORMATION ON MY BTEC LEVEL 3 NATIONAL COURSE
1	The title of the BTEC Level 3 National qualification I am studying is:
2	The length of my course is:
3	The total number of units I will study is:
4	The number of mandatory units I have to study is:
5	The titles of these mandatory units and the dates (or terms) when I will study them are:
6	The main topics I will learn in each mandatory unit include:

IMPORTANT INFORMATION ON MY BTEC LEVEL 3 NATIONAL COURSE	
7	The number of optional units I have to study is:
8	The titles of the optional units I will study are:
9	The main topics I will learn in each optional unit include:
10	Other important aspects of my course are:
11	After I have achieved my BTEC Level 3 National my options include:
12	Useful sources of information I can use to find out more about these options include:

2 Many learners already have information, contacts or direct experiences that relate to their course. For example, you may have a specific interest or hobby that links to a unit, such as being a St John Ambulance cadet if you are studying Public Services. Think about the relevant sources of information you already have access to and complete the table below.

MY INFORMATION SOURCES	
Experts I know	(Who they are, what they know)
My hobbies and interests	(What they are, what they involve)
My job(s)	(Past and present work and work experience, and what I did)
Programmes I like to watch	(What these are, how they relate to my course)

Magazines and/or books I read	(What these are, examples of relevant articles)
ICT sources	(My centre's intranet as well as useful websites)
Other	(Other sources relevant for my particular course and the topics I will be studying)

Step Two: Understand how you are assessed and graded

Case study: Working on a display

Emille and Sean are working on a display for their assignment for Unit 12: Public Health. They have been given the task of presenting information about how HIV is spread and how it can be prevented. Their tutor has arranged that groups of healthcare students deliver health campaigns to other tutor groups in the college. Emille and Sean will present their work to a group of sports students. They have made a PowerPoint presentation about how HIV spreads and the damage it can do to societies. They will also demonstrate the correct way to use a condom. In order that they have up-to-date information, their tutor has arranged for a health promotion officer to visit the learners as a guest speaker.

Both Emille and Sean find the talk very interesting and take notes about how to prevent the spread of HIV. After they have completed their campaign they hand in their assignment on HIV. Emille includes her notes from the talk describing how HIV can be prevented. Sean reads the notes carefully. He then does some additional research to assess the different methods that can be used to promote HIV awareness and protect public health. When Sean hands his work in, he has thoroughly explained how the spread of HIV can be prevented.

Emille is able to achieve P6 of the grading criterion. Sean's extra research enables him to provide sufficient evidence to acheive M3 of the grading criterion. He is therefore able to work towards achieving a merit grade.

Reflection point

There are clear benefits by doing more research. Do you normally do the minimum required, or take your work further?

When writing assignments it is very important to understand the differences between pass, merit and distinction. Look at the examples on the following pages, taken from Unit 3: Health, Safety and Security in Health and Social Care. Students were asked to describe (pass), explain (merit) or evaluate (distinction) how policies and procedures promote health, safety and security in the health and social care workplace.

Match the examples up with the possible grade of pass, merit or distinction. Then highlight the phrase from each example that made you decide on the grade. Consider why you chose each example.

Example 1

- The Health and Safety at Work Act 1974 (HASAWA) is an umbrella piece of legislation that is designed to protect all employees, employers and visitors.

- During my placement I noticed that the Riverside nursery had implemented the Health and Safety at Work Act by instigating a series of procedures to control the spread of infection.

- To reduce the risk of infection they had provided hand cleansing facilities for visitors and staff on arrival as well as ensuring that all staff used aprons and gloves when necessary.

Grade you would allocate ....

Why did you choose this grade?

Example 2

- The Health and Safety at Work Act 1974 (HASAWA) is an umbrella piece of legislation that is designed to protect all employees, employers and visitors.

- During my placement I noticed that the Riverside nursery had implemented the Health and Safety at Work Act by instigating a series of procedures to control the spread of infection.

- The centre had provided hand cleansing facilities for visitors and staff on arrival, requiring people to clean their hands before working with the children.

- This proved very effective as I observed that all visitors to the centre washed their hands before entering and there were fewer case of illness reported than the same time last year.

Grade you would allocate ....

Why did you choose this grade?

Example 3

- The Health and Safety at Work Act 1974 (HASAWA) is an umbrella piece of legislation that is designed to protect all employees, employers and visitors.

- During my placement I noticed that the Riverside nursery had used the Health and Safety at Work Act by providing aprons for the staff when they served meals and the nursery staff used gloves when changing babies' nappies.

Grade you would allocate ....

Why did you choose this grade?

Your assessment

This section looks at the importance of your assignments, how they are graded and how this converts into unit points and UCAS points. Unlike A-levels, there are no externally-set final exams on a BTEC course. Even if you know this because you already have a BTEC First qualification, you should still read this section as now you will be working at a different level.

Your learning is assessed by **assignments**, set by your tutors. You will complete these throughout your course, using many different **assessment methods**, such as real-life case studies, **projects** and presentations. Some assignments may be work-based or **time-constrained** – it depends very much on the vocational area you are studying.

Your assignments are based on **learning outcomes** set by Edexcel. These are listed for each unit in your course specification. You must achieve **all** the learning outcomes to pass each unit.

TOP TIP

Check the learning outcomes for each unit by referring to the course specification – go to www.edexcel.com.

Important skills to help you achieve your grades include:

- researching and analysing information (see page 55)
- using your time effectively (see page 25)
- working co-operatively as a member of a team (see page 49.)

Your grades, unit points and UCAS points

On a BTEC Level 3 National course, assessments that meet the learning outcomes are graded as pass, merit or distinction. The different grades within each unit are set out by Edexcel as **grading criteria** in a **grading grid**. These criteria identify the **higher-level skills** you must demonstrate to achieve a higher grade (see also Step Six – Understand your assessment, on page 35).

All your assessment grades earn **unit points**. The total points you get for all your units determines your final qualification grade(s) – pass, merit or distinction. You get:

- one final grade if you are taking a Certificate or Subsidiary Diploma
- two final grades if you are taking a Diploma
- three final grades if you are taking an Extended Diploma.

Your points and overall grade(s) convert to **UCAS points**, which you need to be accepted onto a degree course. For example, if you achieve three final pass grades for your BTEC Level 3 Extended Diploma, you get 120 UCAS Tariff points. If you achieve three final distinction grades, this increases to 360 – equivalent to three GCE A-levels.

Please note that all UCAS information was correct at the time of going to print, but we would advise that you check the UCAS website for the most up to date information. See page 88 for how to access their website.

Case study: Securing a university place

Chris and Shaheeda both want a university place and have worked hard on their BTEC Level 3 Extended Diploma course.

Chris's final score is 226 unit points, which converts to 280 UCAS Tariff points. Shaheeda has a total score of 228 unit points – just two points more – which converts to 320 UCAS points! This is because a score of between 204

and 227 unit points gives 280 UCAS points, whereas a score of 228 to 251 points gives 320 UCAS points.

Shaheeda is delighted because this increases her chances of getting a place on the degree course she wants. Chris is annoyed. He says if he had realised he would have worked harder on his last assignment to get two points more.

You start to earn points from your first assessment, so you get many benefits from settling in quickly and doing good work from the start. Understanding how **grade boundaries** work also helps you to focus your efforts to get the best possible final grade.

You will be able to discuss your learning experiences, your personal progress and the achievement of your learning objectives in **individual tutorials** with your tutor. These enable you to monitor your progress and overcome temporary difficulties. You can also talk about any worries you have. Your tutor is one of your most important resources and a tutorial gives you their undivided attention.

You can talk through any questions or problems in your tutorials.

Key points

- Your learning is assessed in a variety of ways, such as by assignments, projects and real-life case studies.
- You need to demonstrate specific knowledge and skills to achieve the learning outcomes set by Edexcel. You must achieve all the grading criteria to pass a unit.
- The grading criteria for pass, merit and distinction are shown in a grading grid for the unit. Higher-level skills are needed for higher grades.
- The assessment grades of pass, merit and distinction convert to unit points. The total unit points you receive for the course determines your final overall grade(s) and UCAS points.

TOP TIP

It's always tempting to spend longer on work you like doing and are good at, but focusing on improving your weak areas will do more to boost your overall grade(s).

Action points

1 Find out more about your own course by carrying out this activity.

a) Find the learning outcomes for the units you are currently studying. Your tutor may have given you these, or you can find them in your course specification – go to www.edexcel.com and search for your qualification.

b) Look at the grading grid for the units and identify the way the requirements change for the higher grades. If there are some unfamiliar words, check these in Step Six of this guide (see page 35 onwards).

c) If the unit points system still seems complicated, ask your tutor to explain it.

d) Check the UCAS points you would need for the course or university which interests you.

e) Design a form you can use to record the unit points you earn throughout your course. Keep this up-to-date. Regularly check how your points relate to your overall grade(s), based on the grade boundaries for your qualification. Your tutor can give you this information or you can check it yourself in the course specification.

Step Three: Understand yourself

Case study: Being self-aware

Liu is 17 years old and has just completed the first year of her BTEC National Diploma in Health and Social Care. It is the summer holidays and she is looking for work until she starts her studies again in September. Liu is quite shy and very quiet but she is confident with children.

Liu asks her mum for suggestions about what she could do over the summer. Her mum suggests she makes a list of the skills she has and the types of people she likes to work with. Liu initially finds this task difficult, until she remembers the work experience that she has completed on her course. Liu worked in two different schools with children aged 6 and 9. She also helps to run her local Brownie unit. Liu realises she is happiest when working with school-aged children.

By carefully looking at her own skills she notices that she is always calm in difficult situations, that children find her easy to talk to, and that she enjoys organising new games and activities for them to do. Liu's mum also points out that she is very reliable and professional, never takes time off work and is always dressed appropriately.

With this new knowledge Liu finds the confidence to apply for a job at a holiday play scheme. She manages to sell herself well by highlighting her capabilities and her previous experience. Liu gets the job.

Reflection points

What do you think is your main strength?

How this this help you in a work situation?

What might be weaknesses that you have?

How can you work to improve them?

What skills and qualities do you think an employer would look for in somebody who wants to work with children?

Self-awareness means understanding how you 'tick'. For example, do you prefer practical activities rather than theory? Do you prefer to draw or sketch an idea, rather than write about it?

Self-awareness is important as it makes you less reliant on other people's opinions and gives you confidence in your own judgement. You can also reflect on your actions to learn from your experiences.

Self-awareness also means knowing your own strengths and weaknesses. Knowing your strengths enables you to feel positive and confident about yourself and your abilities. Knowing your weaknesses means you know the areas you need to develop.

You can analyse yourself by looking at...

... your personality and preferences

You may have taken a personality test at your centre. If not, your tutor may recommend one to use, or there are many available online.

Many employers ask job candidates to complete a personality test so that they can match the type of work they are offering to the most suitable candidates. Although these tests can only give a broad indication of someone's personality they may help to avoid mismatches, such as hiring someone who is introverted to work in sales.

... your skills and abilities

To succeed in your assignments, and to progress in a career, requires a number of skills. Some may be vocationally-specific, or professional, skills that you can improve during your course – such as sporting performance on a Sports course. Others are broader skills that are invaluable no matter what you are studying – such as communicating clearly and co-operating with others.

You will work faster and more accurately, and have greater confidence, if you are skilled and proficient. A quick skills check will identify any problem areas.

TOP TIP

Use the Skills Building section on page 77 to identify the skills you need for your course. You'll also find hints and tips for improving any weak areas.

Key points

- You need certain skills and abilities to get the most out of your BTEC Level 3 National course and to develop your career potential.
- Knowing your strengths and weaknesses is a sign of maturity. It gives you greater confidence in your abilities and enables you to focus on areas for improvement.

TOP TIP

You will find more help on developing your skills and abilities in the sections on: Working as a member of a group; Using time wisely; Researching and analysing information; and Making effective presentations.

Action points

1 Gain insight into your own personality by answering each of the following statements *True* or *False* with a tick. Be honest!

		True	False
a)	If someone annoys me, I can tell them about it without causing offence.		
b)	If someone is talking, I often interrupt them to give them my opinion.		
c)	I get really stressed if I'm under pressure.		
d)	I can sometimes become very emotional and upset on other people's behalf.		
e)	I sometimes worry that I can't cope and may make a mess of something.		
f)	I am usually keen, enthusiastic and motivated to do well.		
g)	I enjoy planning and organising my work.		
h)	I find it easy to work and co-operate with other people and take account of their opinions.		
i)	I am easily influenced by other people.		
j)	I often jump to conclusions and judge people and situations on first impressions.		
k)	I prefer to rely on facts and experience rather than following my instincts.		

Now identify which of the skills and qualities in the box below will be really important in your chosen career.

> tact   truthfulness   listening skills
>
> **staying calm under pressure**
>
> empathy with others   self-confidence
>
> initiative   planning and organising
>
> working with others   self-assurance
>
> objective judgements

Use your answers to identify areas you should work on to be successful in the future.

2 As part of the UCAS process, all **higher education** applicants have to write a personal statement. This is different from a CV, which is a summary of achievements that all job applicants prepare. You may have already prepared a CV but not thought about a personal statement. Now is your chance to!

Read the information about personal statement in the box. Then answer these questions:

a) Explain why personal statements are so important for higher education applicants.

b) Why do you think it is important for your personal statement to read well and be error-free?

c) Suggest three reasons why you shouldn't copy a pre-written statement you have found online.

d) Check websites to see what to include in the statement and how to set it out. Go to page 88 to find out how to access useful websites.

e) Prepare a bullet point list of ten personal facts. Focus on your strengths and good reasons why you should be given a place on the higher education course of your choice. If possible, discuss your list with your tutor. Then keep it safely, as it will be useful if you need to write a personal statement later.

Personal statements

This is the information that all higher education applicants have to put in the blank space on their UCAS form. The aim is to sell yourself to admissions tutors. It can be pretty scary, especially if you haven't written anything like it before.

So, where do you start?

First, *never* copy pre-written statements you find online. These are just for guidance. Even worse are websites that offer to write your statement for a fee, and send you a few general, pre-written paragraphs. Forget them all: you can do better!

Imagine you are an admissions tutor with 60 places to offer to 200 applicants. What will you need to read in a personal statement to persuade you to offer the applicant a place?

Most likely, clear explanations about:

- what the applicant can contribute to the course
- why the applicant really wants a place on your course
- what the applicant has done to further his/her own interests in this area, eg voluntary work
- attributes that show this applicant would be a definite bonus – such as innovative ideas, with evidence eg 'I organised a newsletter which we published every three months …'

A personal statement should be well written, with no grammatical or spelling errors and organised into clear paragraphs.

For further guidance, go to page 88 to find out how you will be able to access a number of helpful websites.

Activity: Assessing your skills

Unit 6: Personal Professional Development in Health and Social Care asks you to:

P2: Discuss own knowledge, skills, practice, values, beliefs and career aspirations at the start of the course.

Try to answer the following questions to begin to complete this activity.

1 What makes you who you are? Describe your own morals, your beliefs and the values that are important to you.

2 List some of the skills you feel you already have, i.e. good listener, organised, confident.

3 How could you improve on some of these skills during this course?

4 In the space below write about other life experiences, hobbies, interests and jobs, which you could use to describe who you are, to show your knowledge is more than a collection of exam results?

5 Why choose health and social care? Describe your career aspirations, saying why they are important to you.

Step Four: Use your time wisely

Case study: Getting the balance right

Harry, Jake and Tom are 18 years old. It's Saturday night and Harry and Jake have decided to go out for the night. They have been at home all day playing on their new Xbox. Tom has been working at his local Co-op; his shift started at 8 a.m. and finished at 5 p.m. He is very tired but really feels like joining Harry and Jake for their usual Saturday night out at their local club.

On getting home from work, Tom finds a message asking if he will help coach Scouts football on Sunday morning as the squad's coach has been taken ill. Tom has been volunteering with his local Scout troop and has offered to help coach them for the county Scouts football challenge. Tom is hoping to use his experience volunteering with Scouts to add to his personal statement on his university application to become a paediatric nurse.

Tom also receives a phone call from his girlfriend Maria, another student on his BTEC National Diploma in Health and Social Care course. She asks him if he has finished his Unit 1 assignment, which is due in on Monday. Tom hasn't done the work. As Tom is struggling to understand the work, Maria offers to come over to Tom's house on Saturday night to help him study as she is away all day on Sunday.

Reflection points

What would you prioritise if you were in the same situation?

When you have assignments due, do you plan your time effectively, set targets, prioritise tasks and monitor your progress?

Most learners have to combine course commitments with other responsibilities such as a job (either full- or part-time) and family responsibilities. You will also want to see your friends and keep up your hobbies and interests. Juggling these successfully means you need to be able to use your time wisely.

This involves planning what to do and when to do it to prevent panics about unexpected deadlines. As your course progresses, this becomes even more important as your workload may increase towards the end of a term. In some cases there could be two or more assignments to complete simultaneously. Although tutors try to avoid clashes of this sort, it is sometimes inevitable.

To cope successfully, you need time-management skills, in particular:

- how to organise your time to be more productive
- how to prioritise tasks
- how to overcome time-wasters.

Organising your time

- **Use a diary or wall chart.**
  Using a different colour pen for each, enter:
  - your course commitments, eg assignment dates, tutorials, visits
  - important personal commitments, eg sports matches, family birthdays
  - your work commitments.

TOP TIP

A diary is useful because you can update it as you go, but a wall chart gives you a better overview of your commitments over several weeks. Always keep your diary or chart up-to-date and check ahead regularly so that you have prior warning of important dates.

- **Identify how you currently use your time.**
  - Work out how much time you spend at your centre, at work, at home and on social activities.
  - Identify which commitments are vital and which are optional so you can find extra time if necessary.
- **Plan and schedule future commitments.**
  - Write down any appointments and tasks you must do.
  - Enter assignment review dates and final deadline dates in different colours.
  - This should stop you from arranging a dental appointment on the same morning that you are due to give an important presentation – or planning a hectic social life when you have lots of course work to do.

- **Decide your best times for doing course work.**
  - Expect to do most of your course work in your own time.
  - Work at the time of day when you feel at your best.
  - Work regularly, and in relatively short bursts, rather than once or twice a week for very long stretches.
  - If you're a night owl, allow an hour to 'switch off' before you go to bed.
- **Decide where to work.**
  - Choose somewhere you can concentrate without interruption.
  - Make sure there is space for resources you use, such as books or specialist equipment.
  - You also need good lighting and a good – but not too comfortable – chair.
  - If you can't find suitable space at home, check out your local or college library.
- **Assemble the items you need.**
  - Book ahead to get specific books, journals or DVDs from the library.
  - Ensure you have your notes, handouts and assignment brief with you.
  - Use sticky notes to mark important pages in textbooks or folders.

TOP TIP

Set yourself a target when you start work, so that you feel positive and productive at the end. Always try to end a session when a task is going well, rather than when you are stuck. Then you will be keener to go back to it the next day. Note down outstanding tasks you need to continue with next time.

- **Plan ahead**
  - If anything is unclear about an assignment, ask your tutor for an explanation as soon as you can.
  - Break down long tasks or assignments into manageable chunks, eg find information, decide what to use, create a plan for finished work, write rough draft of first section, etc.
  - Work back from deadline dates so that you allow plenty of time to do the work.
  - Always allow more time than you need. It is better to finish early than to run out of time.

TOP TIP

If you are working on a task as a group, organise and agree times to work together. Make sure you have somewhere to meet where you can work without disturbing other courses or groups.

- **Be self-disciplined.**
  - Don't put things off because you're not in the mood. Make it easier by doing simple tasks first to get a sense of achievement. Then move on to something harder.
  - Plan regular breaks. If you're working hard you need a change of activity to recharge your batteries.
  - If you have a serious problem or personal crisis, talk to your personal tutor promptly.

TOP TIP

Make sure you know the consequences of missing an assignment deadline, as well as the dispensations and exemptions that can be given if you have an unavoidable and serious problem, such as illness.

How to prioritise tasks

Prioritising means doing the most important and urgent task first. Normally this will be the task or assignment with the closest deadline or the one that will most affect your overall course grades.

One way of prioritising is to group tasks into ABC categories.

Category A tasks	These must be done now as they are very important and cannot be delayed, eg completing an assignment to be handed in tomorrow.
Category B tasks	These are jobs you should do if you have time, because otherwise they will rapidly become Category A, eg getting a book that you need for your next assignment.
Category C tasks	These are tasks you should do if you have the time, eg rewriting notes jotted down quickly in a lesson.

Expect to be flexible. For example, if you need to allow time for information to arrive, then send for this first. If you are working in a team, take into account other people's schedules when you are making arrangements.

Avoiding time-wasters

Everyone has days when they don't know where the time has gone. It may be because they were constantly interrupted or because things just kept going wrong. Whatever the reason, the end result is that some jobs don't get done.

If this happens to you regularly, you need to take steps to keep on track.

Some useful tips are:

- **Warn people in advance when you will be working.**
  - Ask them to not interrupt you.
  - If you are in a separate room, shut the door. If someone comes in, make it clear you don't want to talk.
  - If that doesn't work, find somewhere else (or some other time) to work.
- **Switch off your mobile, TV, radio and iPod/ MP3 player.**
  - Don't respond to, or make, calls or texts.
  - If someone rings your home phone, let voicemail answer or ask them to call back later.
- **Be strict with yourself when you are working online.**
  - Don't check your email until you've finished work.
  - Don't get distracted when searching for information.
  - Keep away from social networking sites.
- **Avoid displacement activities.**
  - These are the normally tedious jobs, such as cleaning your computer screen, that suddenly seem far more attractive than working!

Talking to friends can occupy a lot of time.

TOP TIP

The first step in managing your own time is learning to say 'no' (nicely!) if someone asks you to do something tempting when you should be working.

TOP TIP

Benefits to managing your own time include being less stressed (because you are not reacting to problems or crises), producing better work and having time for a social life.

Key points

- Being in control of your time allows you to balance your commitments according to their importance and means you won't let anyone down.
- Organising yourself and your time involves knowing how you spend your time now, planning when and where it is best to work, scheduling commitments and setting sensible timescales to complete your work.
- Knowing how to prioritise means you will schedule work effectively according to its urgency and importance. You will need self-discipline to follow the schedule you have set for yourself.
- Identifying ways in which you may waste time means you can guard against these to achieve your goals more easily.

Action points

1 Start planning your time properly.

a) Find out how many assignments you will have this term, and when you will get them. Put this information into your diary or planner.

b) Update this with your other commitments for the term – both work/course-related and social. Identify possible clashes and decide how to resolve the problem.

c) Identify one major task or assignment you will do soon. Divide it into manageable chunks and decide how long to allow for each chunk, plus some spare time for any problems. If possible, check your ideas with your tutor before you put them into your planner.

2 How good are you at being responsible for your own learning?

a) Fill in the following table. Score yourself out of 5 for each area: where 0 is awful and 5 is excellent. Ask a friend or relative to score you as well. See if you can explain any differences.

	Scoring yourself	Other person's score for you
Being punctual		
Organisational ability		
Tidiness		
Working accurately		
Finding and correcting own mistakes		
Solving problems		
Accepting responsibility		
Working with details		
Planning how to do a job		
Using own initiative		
Thinking up new ideas		
Meeting deadlines		

b) Draw up your own action plan for areas where you need to improve. If possible, talk this through at your next **tutorial** (see page 92).

TOP TIP

Don't waste time doing things that distract you when studying for this course. In a health and social care organisation, time costs money.

Activity: Making the best use of your time

Life is very unpredictable – you never know what is around the corner. Look at the list of common problems that could affect learners and find out how your place of learning deals with them. It is better to be prepared now than to panic if something happens.

Tessa's grandmother has died and she wants to attend the funeral but it will mean she misses a deadline to hand in an assignment. Find out the policy on late submission of work. Are there any exceptions?

What is the difference between a descriptive poster and an analytical essay?

Jasmine doesn't have enough money for the bus fare to get to the centre so she hasn't been attending her lessons. Can the centre pay for her fare?

Kira lent Sam her assignment to read. Sam has handed in her work, which is identical to Kira's, and Kira is now accused of cheating. What is the policy on plagiarism?

Will she have to give up her studies?

Shelly has just found out she is 16 weeks pregnant. This mean she will have the baby in the middle of her second year at the centre. Will Shelly be able to complete the course?

Class 1B have been asked by their tutor to hand in their end-of-year project spiral bound with coloured sheets of paper. Several member of the class cannot afford to present their work in this manner. What should they do?

Dave didn't read the assignment instructions carefully and has submitted a poster on the communication cycle rather than an essay. Can Dave still be awarded a mark even though the work is in a different format?

Step Five: Utilise all your resources

Case study: People as resources

Sinead and Kayleigh are both studying for the BTEC National Certificate in Health and Social Care.

Sinead is the main carer for her 14-year-old brother, who has cerebral palsy. She is responsible for all his daily care as well as getting him to the school bus on time. Sinead wants to work in a residential care home that specialises in caring for people with dementia. She has done one week of work experience at The Oaks residential care home. They were so impressed with her that they have offered her a job when she completes her college course.

Kayleigh lives with her mum and grandmother, who has dementia. Kayleigh's mum looks after her Gran full time. Kayleigh helps her mum when she can and enjoys spending time with her Gran and taking her out whenever possible. Kayleigh really wants to work with children with disabilities.

Sinead has to write an assignment describing the signs and symptoms of dementia.

Kayleigh needs to write about the Disability Discrimination Act 1995. When working together in the library at college they soon realise that they can help each other. Sinead helps Kayleigh understand what it is like to live with a child with disabilities. She suggests that Kayleigh comes home with her and spends some time with her and her brother. Kayleigh invites Sinead home for tea where she can meet her Gran and accompany them both for a walk on the beach. Both Sinead and Kayleigh can use each other as valuable resources.

Reflection points

Do you have any friends who could help you to learn more about your chosen career?

Research the support agencies available for young carers. What resources do they offer to help young people succeed in education?

Your resources are all the things that can help you to be successful in your BTEC Level 3 National qualification, from your favourite website to your study buddy (see page 33) who collects handouts for you if you miss a class.

Your centre will provide essential resources, such as a library with appropriate books and electronic reference sources, the computer network and internet access. You will have to provide basic resources such as pens, pencils and file folders yourself. If you have to buy your own textbooks, look after them carefully so you can sell them on at the end of your course.

Here is a list of resources, with tips for getting the best out of them.

- **Course information**. This includes your course specification, this Study Skills Guide and all information on the Edexcel website relating to your BTEC Level 3 National course. Course information from your centre will include term dates, assignment dates and your timetable. Keep everything safely so you can refer to it whenever you need to clarify something.
- **Course materials**. These include course handouts, printouts, your own notes and textbooks. Put handouts into an A4 folder as soon as you get them. Use a separate folder for each unit you study.

TOP TIP

Filing notes and handouts promptly means they don't get lost, will stay clean and uncrumpled and you won't waste time looking for them.

- **Stationery**. You need pens and pencils, a notepad, a hole puncher, a stapler and sets of dividers. Dividers should be clearly labelled to help you store and quickly find notes, printouts and handouts. Your notes should be headed and dated, and those from your own research must also include your source (see Step Eight – page 55 onwards.)
- **People**. Your tutors, specialist staff at college, classmates, your employer and work colleagues, your relatives and friends are all valuable resources. Many will have particular skills or work in the vocational area that you are studying. Talking to other learners can help to clarify issues that there may not have been time to discuss fully in class.

A **study buddy** is another useful resource as they can make notes and collect handouts if you miss a session. (Remember to return the favour when they are away.)

Always be polite when you are asking people for information. Prepare the questions first and remember that you are asking for help, not trying to get them to do the work for you! If you are interviewing someone for an assignment or project, good preparations are vital. (See Step Eight – page 55 onwards.)

If someone who did the course before you offers help, be careful. It is likely the course requirements will have changed. Never be tempted to copy their assignments (or someone else's). This is **plagiarism** – a deadly sin in the educational world (see also Step Six – page 35.)

TOP TIP

A positive attitude, an enquiring mind and the ability to focus on what is important will have a major impact on your final result.

Key points

- Resources help you to achieve your qualification. Find out what resources you have available to you and use them wisely.
- Have your own stationery items.
- Know how to use central facilities and resources such as the library, learning resource centres and your computer network. Always keep to the policy on IT use in your centre.
- People are a key resource – school or college staff, work colleagues, members of your class, friends, family and people who are experts in their field.

TOP TIP

Learn to be your own best resource by developing the skills you need to work quickly and accurately.

Action points

1 **a)** List the resources you will need to complete your course successfully. Identify which ones will be provided by your school or college, and which you need to supply yourself.

  b) Go through your list again and identify the resources you already have (or know how to access) and those you don't.

  c) Compare your list with a friend's and decide how to obtain and access the resources you need. Add any items to your list that you forgot.

  d) List the items you still need to get and set a target date for doing this.

2 'Study buddy' schemes operate in many centres. Find out if this applies to your own centre and how you can make the best use of it.

  In some you can choose your study buddy, in others people are paired up by their tutor.
  • Being a study buddy might mean just collecting handouts when the other person is absent, and giving them important news.
  • It may also mean studying together and meeting (or keeping contact by phone or email) to exchange ideas and share resources.

With a study buddy you can share resources and stay on top of the course if you're ever away.

Activity: Using resources

Resources come in many shapes and forms. Looking back at the case study of Sinead and Kayleigh, think about the other resources they could have used to help them complete their assignments.

1 From the examples below underline the resources they used to complete the tasks set.

Sinead asked the care home manager at her placement if she could interview her about the signs and symptoms of dementia.

Sinead interviewed a resident of a care home about their life with dementia

Sinead borrowed a textbook about dementia from the centre library.

Kayleigh got a DVD out from the centre library which talked about living with people with disabilities.

Kayleigh researched the Disability Discrimination Act 1995 online.

Kayleigh managed to get a placement at a school for children with disabilities.

Kayleigh and Sinead together approached their local council to ask about how it implements the Disability Discrimination Act 1995 and what facilities it offers for people with dementia.

2 Now try and think of other resources that they could have used that have not previously been mentioned.

Step Six: Understand your assessment

Case study: Gaining the marks you need

Claire is in the second year of an extended Diploma in Health and Social Care and has been offered a place at University. The entry requirements are high and she must achieve a final grade of at least DMM.

Her first year grades showed a steady movement as she gained a greater understanding how assignments were to be tackled and, by the end of the year, she had hit her target of achieving merits and distinctions.

This year, however, she is finding some of the units very challenging. She is having to work even harder to achieve her goal, but realises that it will be worth all the effort in the end.

Before starting on an assignment, Claire carefully reads through the brief and plans how she is going to tackle the tasks. She confirms with her tutor that she is on the right track and sets review targets.

'I don't have any real problem producing assignments because they always focus on topics that we've been taught in class. The good thing about a BTEC assignment is that you can check progress with your tutor and, if necessary, improve your grades after it's been marked. This helped a lot when in my first year as some of my early assignments were a bit shaky. I only got pass grades. My tutor added feedback guidance on how to improve and I upped my grades to merit and distinction.

When you start on a BTEC course it's important to understand that all assignment briefs are laid out in a standard way. To do well, you need to pick up on some of the special words/terms used in them, particularly command words such as identify interpret, discuss, analyse.'

Reflection points

When presented with a task can you plan a solution?

Do you know how to carry out effective research and manage your time?

What is constructive criticism and how can it help you improve your grades?

Why are assignment briefs very rarely 'brief'?

Being successful on any BTEC Level 3 National course means first understanding what you must do in your assignments – and then doing it.

Your assignments focus on topics you have already covered in class. If you've attended regularly, you should be able to complete them confidently.

However, there are some common pitfalls it's worth thinking about. Here are tips to avoid them:

- Read the instructions (the assignment brief) properly and several times before you start.
- Make sure you understand what you are supposed to do. Ask if anything is unclear.

- Complete every part of a task. If you ignore a question, you can't meet the grading criteria.
- Prepare properly. Do your research or reading before you start. Don't guess the answers.
- Communicate your ideas clearly. You can check this by asking someone who doesn't know the subject to look at your work.
- Only include relevant information. Padding out answers makes it look as if you don't know your subject.
- Do the work earlier rather than later to avoid any last-minute panics.
- Pay attention to advice and feedback that your tutor has given you.

The assignment 'brief'

This may be longer than its name implies! The assignment brief includes all the instructions for an assignment and several other details, as you can see in the table below.

What will you find in a BTEC Level 3 National assignment brief?	
Content	**Details**
Title	This will link to the unit and learning outcomes
Format/style	Written assignment, presentation, demonstration, etc
Preparation	Read case study, do research, etc
Learning outcomes	These state the knowledge you must demonstrate to obtain a required grade
Grading criterion/ criteria covered	eg P1/M1/D1
Individual/group work	Remember to identify your own contribution in any group work
Feedback	Tutor, peer review
Interim review dates	Dates to see your tutor
Final deadline	Last submission date

Your centre's rules and regulations

Your centre will have several policies and guidelines about assignments, which you need to check carefully. Many, such as those listed below, relate to Edexcel policies and guidelines.

- The procedure to follow if you have a serious problem and can't meet a deadline. An extension may be granted.
- The penalty for missing a deadline without good reason.
- The penalty for copying someone else's work. This is usually severe, so never share your work (or CDs or USB flash drive) with anyone else, and don't borrow theirs.
- **Plagiarism** is also serious misconduct. This means copying someone's work or quoting from books and websites and pretending it is your own work.
- The procedure to follow if you disagree with the grade you are given.

Understanding the question or task

There are two aspects to a question or task. The first is the **command words**, which are described below. The second is the **presentation instructions**, which is what you are asked to do – don't write a report when you should be producing a chart!

Command words, such as 'explain', 'describe', 'analyse', 'evaluate', state how a question must be answered. You may be asked to 'describe' something at pass level, but you will need to do more, perhaps 'analyse' or 'evaluate', to achieve merit or distinction.

Many learners fail to achieve higher grades because they don't realise the difference between these words. Instead of analysing or evaluating they give an explanation instead. Adding more details won't achieve a higher grade – you need to change your whole approach to the answer.

The **grading grid** for each unit of your course gives you the command words, so that you know what to do to achieve a pass, merit or distinction. The tables that follow show you what is usually required when you see a particular command word. These are just examples to guide you as the exact response will depend on the question. If you have any doubts, check with your tutor before you start work.

There are two important points to note.

- A command word, such as 'create' or 'explain', may be repeated in the grading criteria for different grades. In these cases the complexity or range of the task itself increases at the higher grades.
- Command words vary depending on your vocational area. So Art and Design grading grids may use different command words from Applied Science, for example.

TOP TIP

Look at this section again when you get your first assignment and check the command words against these explanations.

To obtain a pass grade

To achieve a pass you must usually demonstrate that you understand the important facts relating to a topic and can state these clearly and concisely.

Command words for a pass	Meaning
Create (or produce)	Make, invent or construct an item.
Describe	Give a clear, straightforward description that includes all the main points and links these together logically.
Define	Clearly explain what a particular term means and give an example, if appropriate, to show what you mean.
Explain … how/why	Set out in detail the meaning of something, with reasons. It is often helpful to give an example of what you mean. Start with the topic then give the 'how' or 'why'.
Identify	Distinguish and state the main features or basic facts relating to a topic.
Interpret	Define or explain the meaning of something.
Illustrate	Give examples to show what you mean.
List	Provide the information required in a list rather than in continuous writing.
Outline	Write a clear description that includes all the main points but avoid going into too much detail.
Plan (or devise)	Work out and explain how you would carry out a task or activity.
Select (and present) information	Identify relevant information to support the argument you are making and communicate this in an appropriate way.
State	Write a clear and full account.
Undertake	Carry out a specific activity.
Examples:	
Identify the main features on a digital camera.	
Outline the steps to take to carry out research for an assignment.	

To obtain a merit grade

To obtain a merit you must prove that you can apply your knowledge in a specific way.

Command words for a merit	Meaning
Analyse	Identify separate factors, say how they relate to each other and how each one relates to the topic.
Classify	Sort your information into appropriate categories before presenting or explaining it.
Compare and contrast	Identify the main factors that apply in two or more situations and explain the similarities and differences or advantages and disadvantages.
Demonstrate	Provide several relevant examples or appropriate evidence which support the arguments you are making. In some vocational areas this may also mean giving a practical performance.
Discuss	Provide a thoughtful and logical argument to support the case you are making.
Explain (in detail)	Provide details and give reasons and/or evidence to clearly support the argument you are making.
Implement	Put into practice or operation. You may also have to interpret or justify the effect or result.
Interpret	Understand and explain an effect or result.
Justify	Give appropriate reasons to support your opinion or views and show how you arrived at these conclusions.
Relate/report	Give a full account, with reasons.
Research	Carry out a full investigation.
Specify	Provide full details and descriptions of selected items or activities.
Examples: Compare and contrast the performance of two different digital cameras. Explain in detail the steps to take to research an assignment.	

To obtain a distinction grade

To obtain a distinction you must prove that you can make a reasoned judgement based on appropriate evidence.

Command words for a distinction	Meaning
Analyse	Identify the key factors, show how they are linked and explain the importance and relevance of each.
Assess	Give careful consideration to all the factors or events that apply and identify which are the most important and relevant, with reasons.
Comprehensively explain	Give a very detailed explanation that covers all the relevant points and give reasons for your views or actions.
Critically comment	Give your view after you have considered all the evidence, particularly the importance of both the relevant positive and negative aspects.
Evaluate	Review the information and then bring it together to form a conclusion. Give evidence to support each of your views or statements.
Evaluate critically	Review the information to decide the degree to which something is true, important or valuable. Then assess possible alternatives, taking into account their strengths and weaknesses if they were applied instead. Then give a precise and detailed account to explain your opinion.
Summarise	Identify/review the main, relevant factors and/or arguments so that these are explained in a clear and concise manner.
Examples:	
Assess ten features commonly found on a digital camera.	
Analyse your own ability to carry out effective research for an assignment.	

TOP TIP

Check that you understand exactly how you need to demonstrate each of the learning outcomes specified in the assignment.

Responding positively

Assignments enable you to demonstrate what you know and how you can apply it. You should respond positively to the challenge and give it your best shot. Being well organised and having confidence in your own abilities helps too, and this is covered in the next section.

Key points

- Read instructions carefully so that you don't make mistakes that can easily be avoided, such as only doing part of the set task.
- Note the assignment deadline on your planner and any interim review dates. Schedule work around these dates to make the most of reviews with your tutor.
- Check your centre's policies relating to assignments, such as how to obtain an extension or query a final grade.
- Expect command words and/or the complexity of a task to be different at higher grades, because you have to demonstrate higher-level skills.

TOP TIP

All your assignments will relate to topics you have covered and work you have done in class. They're not meant to be a test to catch you out.

Action points

1 Check your ability to differentiate between different types of command words by doing this activity.
   a) Prepare a brief description of your usual lifestyle (pass level).
   b) Describe and justify your current lifestyle (merit level).
   c) Critically evaluate your current lifestyle (distinction level).

It would be a good idea to check that your answer is accurate and appropriate by showing it to your tutor at your next tutorial.

TOP TIP

When presenting evidence for an assessment, think about the person who will be looking through it. Plan your 'pitch' well and make it easy for the assessor to match your evidence against the grading criteria.

Sample assignment

Note about assignments

All learners are different and will approach their assignment in different ways.
The sample assignment that follows shows how one learner answered a brief to achieve pass, merit and distinction level criteria. The learner work whose just one way in which grading criteria can be evidenced. There are no standard or set answers. If you produce the required evidence for each task then you will achieve the grading criteria covered by the assignment.

Make sure that you complete the front sheet fully, accurately and neatly. Fill in all the boxes and spaces. Write your name in full.

Hand work in before or on the set completion date. Find out about the centre policy on meeting deadlines.

Before submitting your work, ask your assessor to check it is all there. You may have forgotten some evidence.

For a particular criterion, check that your evidence adequately covers the content of the unit as described in the assessment section of the unit. You can ask your assessor to check for you.

Learner name		Assessor name	
Louisa Jameson		Maud Silversmith	
Date issued	**Completion date**		**Submitted on**
24 September 2010	3 December 2010		2 December 2010
Qualification		**Unit**	
BTEC Level 3 Extended Diploma in Health and Social Care		Unit 4: Development Through the Life Stages	

Assignment title	Patterns of development through the life stages

In this assignment you will have opportunities to provide evidence against the following criteria.
Indicate the page numbers where the evidence can be found.

Criteria reference	To achieve the criteria the evidence must show that the student is able to:	Task no.	Page numbers
P1	describe physical, intellectual, emotional and social development for each of the life stages of an individual	1	1
M1	discuss the nature–nurture debate in relation to the development of an individual	1	2
D1	evaluate how nature and nurture may affect the physical, intellectual, emotional and social development of two stages of the development of an individual	1	2

Learner declaration

I certify that the work submitted for this assignment is my own and research sources are fully acknowledged.

Learner signature: *Louisa Jameson*   Date: *2 December 2010*

This table tells you what evidence you must produce to achieve the criteria. Your assessor will tell you what to do to achieve this.

Make sure that any evidence you present is your own and not copied from other people's work. Acknowledge any information you used at the end of your work by referencing.

Assignment brief

By relating the assignment tasks to health and social care settings, scenarios help you solve some problems that you could face in the real world of health and social care.

When completing the assignment, remember the title as this can help you stay focused and on the right path.

Unit title	Unit 4: Development Through the Life Stages
Qualification	BTEC Level 3 Extended Diploma in Health and Social Care
Start date	24 September 2010
Deadline date	3 December 2010
Assessor	Maud Silversmith

Assignment title	Patterns of development through the life stages

The purpose of this assignment is to assess learner understanding of the recognised pattern of development throughout the human lifespan, and the factors which may affect this.

Scenario
You are working as a health visitor attached to a local health centre, concerned with supporting a number of individuals within the local community. The Primary Care Trust has asked you to produce a report for student health visitors on how various factors may affect the recognised pattern of lifespan development. You have decided to use a live case as an example for the students, changing all details which would breach confidentiality.

You have chosen to describe the development of Farah Hussein, a 72-year-old woman who lives with her son and his wife in an extended family unit. Farah contracted tuberculosis of the spine as a young girl of six in Pakistan; her family emigrated when she was 15 and she has lived in North Wales ever since. Farah has lived a full and happy life so far; she has a supportive family, and before her husband died two years ago, a happy marriage. Farah has always required the use of a walking aid, but is now confined to a wheelchair due to the onset of osteoarthritis.

Task
Produce a report which:
- describes the recognised pattern of human growth and development
- discusses the nature–nurture debate in relation to Farah's overall development
- evaluates how nature and nurture may have affected Farah's overall development at two of her life stages.

This provides evidence for: P1, M1, D1

When an assignment uses terms such as describe, discuss and evaluate you will have the opportunity to produce evidence at a pass, merit or distinction level.

A wide range of sources should be used to support assignment work; try to vary your methods of finding relevant research and not just relying on the internet.

Textbooks are a valuable source of information as they are written specifically for your course and your level of learning. Textbooks should only be used to support research and not relied on totally. You should always use the latest versions of published texts whenever possible.

Sources of information

Textbooks
Feldman R – *Development Through the Lifespan, 4th Edition* (Pearson, 2008) ISBN 9780136084853
Meggitt C – *Child Development: An Illustrated Guide* (Heinemann, 2006) ISBN 0435420-488
Squire G (Editor) – *BTEC National Children's Care, Learning and Development Student Book* (Pearson Education, 2007) ISBN 9780435499099
Stretch B and Whitehouse M (Editors) – *BTEC National Health and Social Care Book 1* (Pearson Education, 2010) ISBN 9781846907463

Journals
Community Care
Nursing Times
Nursery World

Websites
www.communitycare.co.uk – *Community Care* magazine
www.dh.gov.uk –Department of Health
www.nursingtimes.net – *Nursing Times* magazine

This brief has beeen verified as being fit for purpose				
Assessor	Maud Silversmith			
Signature	*Maud Silversmith*		Date	*12 September 2010*
Internal verifier	John Peters			
Signature	*Felicity Adams*		Date	*12 September 2010*

Appropriate Health and Care journals will detail relevant research and modern practices and evaluate their application and relevance to Health and Care settings.

The internet will provide a world of information about all aspects of care, but sources should always be researched based and supported by relevant evidence. All too often issues around health and care are merely anecdotal and not always based on facts.

Sample learner work

The appropriate use of headings and subheadings allows you to focus your work on a particular area, which in turn helps indicate which section of an assignment is being addressed.

The use of correct terminology in an assignment demonstrates that you have a clear understanding of course content and can apply your work to Health and Care settings.

Sample learner work: page 1

Patterns of development through the life stages

Task:

Produce a report which:

- describes the recognised pattern of human growth and development
- examines the nature–nurture debate in relation to Farah's overall development
- evaluates how nature and nurture may affect Farah's overall development at two of her life stages

A report on the lifespan development of Farah Hussein, aged 72 years

Section 1: Patterns of human growth and development

Farah developed within accepted lifespan patterns, from conception to birth. There is no evidence that her development, from the fusion of ova and sperm through the stages of embryo and foetus, were affected by detrimental factors. The assumption is that Farah would have been delivered between 38 and 40 weeks following a normal labour. There is no evidence in the case study of abnormal birth patterns or issues following birth in the neonatal period to indicate a cause for concern. Farah lived with both parents, which would have supported her emotional and social development.

Farah's physical development was within normal parameters until the age of six years when she contracted tuberculosis of the spine (Potts Disease). This affected Farah's physical development in that, in addition to the severe pain she suffered, she was left with curvature of the spine, and was unable to participate in sport or gymnastic activities at school. Furthermore, her extended stay in hospital may have meant that Farah's social and emotional development was affected, making her more dependent upon adults than would have been expected. Children between the ages of five and seven are developing independence and preparing for school; therefore an extended stay in hospital, combined with the treatment regime for tuberculosis, may have contributed to a reduction in the confidence and self-reliance described by child development experts. Unless Farah received tuition while in hospital, and there is no evidence of this in the case study, her cognitive and language development may have been delayed. If we consider the theories of cognitive psychologists such as Jean Piaget, we can see that children need to interact with the environment to fully achieve the developmental norms: 'children are active learners' (Snaith M and Tassoni P, 2007, p. 255). In the active stage of her illness, Farah would have found discovery learning difficult, thus leading to the conclusion that her cognitive and language development would have required additional support in order for her to reach the expected milestones.

Farah emigrated with her parents to North Wales at the age of 15, at which time she would have been progressing through puberty and experiencing adolescence. She would have been continuing to develop secondary sexual characteristics as her body prepared itself for reproduction. Adolescence can be traumatic for some young people. Erikson (1968) described the adolescent crisis; amongst the symptoms may be found confusion. In the case of Farah Hussein, her confusion and threat to self-identity may have increased through the period of emigration and resettlement in a new country. This may have been further compounded by moving into a bilingual setting where at least one of the languages, Welsh, would have been unknown to both Farah and her parents. In addition, there may have been the communication barrier of strong regional accents that were unfamiliar to Farah and her family. Other effects on development may have included the differences in culture, perhaps leading to misunderstandings and marginalisation of the family.

References should be evident in all pieces of extended text, as they demonstrate that you have undertaken research to support your work. Always use a recognised method of referencing.

When you have used references in your work, complete the piece of work with a reference list indicating the sources you have used.

When there may be several definitions of a subject to be addressed, it is good practice to highlight and reference the particular definition you are using in your work.

The use of bullet points and/or short concise sentences can enhance the overall presentation of the work.

Sample learner work: page 2

Farah reached adulthood, married and produced at least one child, despite her spinal problems, and has lived a full and happy life. Therefore we must conclude that although she experienced illness in young childhood and the trauma of emigration in adolescence, Farah Hussein has progressed through her life course at appropriate stages and maturation has been sufficient to allow her a 'normal' life. Her current diagnosis of osteoarthritis has compounded the effects of the spinal tuberculosis, rendering her physically disabled. Nevertheless, Farah may retain her ego-integrity (Erikson, 1968) due to her happy family life and supportive family.

Section 2: An examination of the nature–nurture debate in relation to Farah's overall development
Childhood: Childhood is defined as four years to nine years for the purposes of this report.

Physical development:
Normal patterns of physical development at this age will include:

Fine motor movements:

Age	Pattern of development
4 years	Threads small beads Builds towers of ten bricks and makes bridges Holds pencil with good control in adult fashion Draws recognisable houses
5 years	Threads large needle alone and sews real stitches Good pencil control in writing and drawing using pencils and paint brushes Colours pictures neatly staying within lines
By 8 years	Can build tall straight towers using bricks Drawings and pictures show increased recognisable detail Handwriting is even and may start to be joined Ties and unties laces

Information adapted from Butcher J., in Squires G., Editor, 2007, p. 102

Gross Motor Movements

Age	Pattern of development
4–5 years	Steady stride, arms used in walking action Can walk along a narrow line Runs lightly on toes
6–7 years	Catches ball by holding both hands in cup-shape Good balance both when moving and when static Co-ordinated jumping – can jump a distance
By 8 years	Precise gross motor movements e.g. can walk along a line with arms outstretched for balance. Expert rider of a two wheeled bicycle

Information adapted from Butcher J., in Squires G., Editor, 2007, p. 102

The use of tables helps a clear and concise structure within which work can be presented.

When you have used references in your work, complete the piece of work with a reference list indicating the sources you have used.

Be careful not to assume too much, as just because something wasn't evident it doesn't mean it wasn't there. Research cannot explain everything.

A high standard of work will show evidence of being able to introduce relevant information from other Health and Care course units to support your findings.

Sample learner work: page 3

Farah Hussein developed spinal tuberculosis at the age of six years. This infection would have had a dramatic effect on her physical development. For example, the extreme pain caused by the disease in both the lumbar spine and the related muscles would have inhibited any physical activity as the young Farah would not have wanted to move. Furthermore, the infective invasion of the area would have inhibited the bone growth and created distortions of the spine as it grew. Gross motor movements would have been reduced permanently as evidenced by the fact that the subject had used a walking aid for the rest of her life. In addition, as Farah would have been encouraged to remain in bed while in hospital, the enforced lack of exercise would have reduced both muscle strength and mass. The reduction of movement would have had an adverse effect on bone density in the growing child. As there is no evidence of physical problems before the age of six, we must conclude that physical development (as identified by the charts on page 2 of this report) would have been within the recognised developmental norms, and Farah would have met the milestones for her age and stage. Following the onset of the infection, her development would have been arrested.

Intellectual and language development:
There is no evidence of any learning disability or cognitive impairment, therefore it must be assumed that intellectual development continued within accepted parameters up until the age of six. Furthermore, the illness in itself did not affect the brain or its functions and we must assume that Farah is of at least average intelligence. Nevertheless, the reduced physical activity enforced by the infection would adversely affect opportunities to explore and discover, thus reducing the accumulation of knowledge by the young Farah. Again, the long stay in hospital would have provided the young child with a limited circle of friends with whom to interact. In addition, language skills may have therefore been delayed if staff were too busy to spend time communicating with her. However, there is no evidence of any difficulty in this area, and one can assume that the family visited regularly to compensate for any lack on the part of the staff.

Emotional and social development:
Up until the age of six we can assume that Farah would have met the developmental norms in this area. 'Children at this age have become independent and sensible, showing a sense of humour and choosing their own friends.' (Butcher J., in Squires G., Editor, 2007, p. 109). We can assume that Farah interacted with local children and also siblings and relatives. She would have formed multiple attachments with her primary carers, any siblings and other members of the family group. However, her enforced stay in hospital during the acute stage of her illness would have caused separation from close family, even if visits were daily. Freud believed that early childhood experiences have a profound effect on the formation of the personality. It could be suggested, in keeping with this view, that the separation resulted in Farah's developing independence being reduced. Alternatively, she could have become more self-reliant, drawing on the reserves provided by a close family network to deal with her ordeal.

Older age:
As Farah received treatment for the infection, her life course has not been affected. She is still living at the age of 72, having married and produced a child. We can assume from this that the infection did not restrict Farah's social skills or her reproductive ability. Her physical disability has continued to limit her independent mobility and place some restrictions on her social life, in that she will need support to make visits to friends or go shopping. Her disability has been increased through the onset of osteoarthritis, which affects the joints and can extend to the spine. As she is now using a wheelchair, the house will have to be further adapted.

The combination of the effects of the infection and the natural reduction in mobility experienced by many older people may reduce Farah's confidence and self-esteem, particularly as she becomes more reliant on family members to perform personal care. In addition, the loss of her partner may have induced a separation anxiety (Bowlby, 1950), if this has brought with it a loss of status experienced by some widows.

In conclusion, it can be seen that the infection has had an effect on Farah's development in both of the described life stages. Arrested physical development has meant that Farah has not walked unaided from the age of six, which would have prevented her participation in sports and other occupations of life. These would include running for a bus and dancing, for example. The use of a walking aid could have made her feel

A conclusion gives you the opportunity to tie up your findings by offering an explanation for the areas you have addressed in the text.

If you mention an author in your text you must reference where you have found this evidence.

If you mention someone's theory in the text, make sure it is relevant and not just thrown in for effect.

Never introduce another theory in your closing paragraph unless you have fully described the theory somewhere else in the text.

Sample learner work: page 4

conspicuous with a corresponding effect on self-image with a reduction in self-esteem. It could be argued that arrested development was entirely due to an infection and is therefore wholly due to nurture. How she dealt with the issues may be entirely due to her supportive family and good medical care, meaning that nurture was also responsible for her happy and productive life. However, some psychologists, for example Eyesnck (1916–97), said that people are born with personality traits that affect how they deal with situations. We could argue from this that although the infection was due to environment, after Farah contracted the disease her inherited ability to deal with situations enabled her to live a productive life. She therefore dealt with her arrested development according to her natural ability, supported by a positive environment.

Experts who support the nature view say that intelligence and the ability to understand situations through reasoning is inborn; supporters of the nurture view believe that children would not achieve their full potential without a supportive environment. This is known as the nature–nurture debate. It could be seen that much of Farah's development, particularly from the age of six, was shaped by her environment, both positive and negative. Her current health status is partially due to her infection, which reduced the rate of physical development, but also the onset of rheumatic disease, which tends to be inherited.

Therefore, Farah Hussein is, as are we all, a product of nature and nurture. Maturation theory states that we develop according to our pre-determined programming, but this does not allow for a hostile environment which 'trips the wires' and re-routes the programme. Development is holistic; one area has an effect on another, the combination of nature and nurture.

Bibliography
Books
Adolescence Volume 301995
Butcher J. (Editor Squires G.), *National Diploma Children's Care Learning and Development* (Heinemann, 2007)
Snaith M and Tassoni P. (Editor Squires G.), *National Diploma Children's Care Learning and Development* (Heinemann, 2007)

Websites
www.allpsych.com/personalitysynopsis/eyesnck

Make sure that you use a wide range of research sources; do not rely on one textbook to supply all the information you need.

Sample assessor's comments

Your assessor will write either "Yes" or "No" in this box to let you know if you have achieved the criteria.

Detailing what you enjoyed and also any problems that you had will help you in future assignments, as you will know what to do differently to avoid similar problems.

For any assignment, always check that you are achieving the pass (P) criteria. To achieve an overall pass for a unit, you must get all the Ps signed off.

Qualification	BTEC Level 3 Extended Diploma in Health and Social Care	Year	2010–11
Unit number and title	Unit 4: Development Through the Life Stages	Learner name	Louisa Jameson

Grading criteria		Achieved?
P1 describe physical, intellectual, emotional and social development for each of the life stages of an individual		N
M1 discuss the nature–nurture debate in relation to the development of an individual		y
D1 evaluate how nature and nurture may affect the physical, intellectual, emotional and social development of two stages of the development of an individual		Y

Learner feedback

I really enjoyed completing this assignment because it gave me the opportunity to consider the type of case I could be involved with, when I achieve my ambition to become a Health Visitor. I actually enjoy writing reports, when they allow me to apply the theory to real cases. I feel that I have an understanding of the main issues and have demonstrated this in my work.

Assessor feedback

Well done Louisa, I can see that you have worked hard on this assignment. You have demonstrated a clear understanding of the main issues and discussed them in a mature and intelligent manner. There is evidence of description, explanation and evaluation in your work. You missed out on **P1** however because you failed to extend your work to the final stages of life; please see the action plan for my further comments. For **M1** there is a clear explanation of the potential effects of delayed/arrested development on your two chosen life stages and for **D1** there is evidence of evaluation but this could have been extended; please see me in tutorial to discuss this.

Action plan

You have missed out on **P1** as you did not extend your argument far enough through the life stages. You need to be careful to make sure your answer covers all aspects of the grading criteria for that task.

You could also improve your evaluations (**D1**). Although you have referred to the main points, there are places where these could have been extended; for example your reference to maturation theory could have included more detail with reference to Farah Hussein; nevertheless, your discussion is clear and accurate, well done. It is good practice to include references in text where appropriate. While you have done this, you could have extended your inclusion, for example, you mention both Piaget and Eyesnck but do not include a direct reference for either theorist. You should also have included your sources for Piaget in your bibliography. Overall a good effort. Please note my comments and use them to progress even further

Assessor signature	Maud Silversmith	Date	17 December 2010
Learner signature	Louisa Jameson	Date	17 December 2010

You should always read and take note of the assessor's feedback. Here the learner has not completed all the tasks to the required standard. She could still improve her work and the assessor outlines this here.

The assessor shows how things can be improved in future assignments in the action plan.

Step Seven: Work productively as a member of a group

Case study: Working as a team

Jake is a learner on the BTEC National Diploma in Health and Social Care and has a part-time job at weekends at a large supermarket, working in the warehouse. The manager asks Jake and five other members of staff to form a team. He asks the team to come up with recommendations for how one part of the warehouse could be redesigned to make it easier for those who work in that area to assemble goods for home delivery.

The manager selects the six members based on their individual skills. The team meet for the first time and introduce themselves. Jake is creative, Bella has good leadership skills, Ben is very practical and good at getting things done, Joelle is good at planning and anticipating problems, Emily is skilled at design and Alex is hard working and always sees things through to the end. Bella is asked by the manager to be the team leader.

During their meetings Bella always listens to the opinions of other members of the team and always praises and encourages others if they produce good work. She discusses ideas and criticises constructively.

In the current layout of the area that the team are looking at, products are positioned in alphabetical order. The order assemblers working in this area simply collect the order to be assembled and start at the A's to pick the order. The team notice that some products are ordered far more frequently than others, therefore they recommend that the layout be changed so that the fastest selling lines are positioned at the beginning of the flow, with the slower lines at the end. As a result of this reorganisation, the average time taken for order assemblers to put together an order is reduced, which significantly increases productivity. The manager is delighted with the team's work and plans more project work based on the work of effective teams.

Reflection points

Why do you think it is important for a team to have a clear goal before they start work?

Why is it important for team members to possess different skills to one another?

If Bella was not a good communicator and did not allow anyone to express their points of view, how do you think this would this affect the overall success of the team?

In your private life, you can choose your own friends, whereas at work you are paid to work alongside many people; whether you like them or not.

This applies at school or college too. Hopefully, by now, you've outgrown wanting to only work with your best friends on every project.

You may not be keen on everyone in your team, but you should still be pleasant and co-operative.

This may be harder if you are working with a partner than in a large group.

Sometimes you may be the group leader. This may inspire you, or fill you with dread. You won't be expected to develop team-leader skills overnight, but it helps if you know the basics.

First, you should understand how groups and teams work and why good teamwork is considered vital by employers.

Working in groups and teams

If you have a full- or part-time job, you already belong to a working group, or team. At school or college your class is an example of a working group.

All working groups have some common characteristics:

- doing the same type of work – though in the workplace you probably have different roles or responsibilities
- a group leader or supervisor
- a reason for working together, such as studying for the same qualification or tackling an area of work too large for someone to do alone
- group members are dependent on each other in some way; at work you may have to cover someone's workload if they are absent
- group members concentrate on their individual achievements and success.

A team is different. As a team member you have a specific objective to achieve **together** – and this is more important than the goals of individual team members.

> **TOP TIP**
>
> Understanding how groups and teams function will help you be a better team worker and a better team leader.

These are the characteristics of a team.

- Team members have a team goal which is more important than any personal goals.
- Team members have complementary skills so that the team can achieve more than individuals working alone could achieve.
- Work is allocated to play to each person's strengths and talents.
- The team members give each other encouragement and support.
- There is collective responsibility for achieving the goal.

A good team leader acts as facilitator and motivator, and gives practical support and guidance.

Working in a team has many benefits. Team members can learn from each other and combine their skills to do a better job more quickly. Working with other people is often more enjoyable than working alone, too. Many industries rely heavily on efficient group working, from IT teams to health workers and the emergency services.

> **TOP TIP**
>
> Focusing on the task rather than on personalities is the first step in learning to work with different people, whose views may not match your own.

Being a good team member

Everyone wants team members who are talented, positive, cheerful and full of energy. These are the key areas to focus on if you wish to be a good team member.

- **Your social skills.** This includes being courteous, treating other people as you wish to be treated, saying 'please' when you want something and thanking people who do you a favour.

- **Your temperament**. Expect people to have different views and opinions from you and don't take offence if someone disagrees with you. If you lose your temper easily, learn to walk away before you say something you may regret.

- **Your communication skills.** This includes talking and listening!
  Practise saying what you mean clearly, accurately and succinctly.
  Be prepared to give good reasons to justify your arguments and ideas.
  Allow people to finish what they're saying, without interruption, before you talk. Never shout people down. Think before you speak so that you don't upset people with tactless remarks. If you inadvertently do so, apologise.

There are many benefits to be gained from working as a team.

- **Your commitment.** Always keep your promises and never let anyone down when they are depending upon you. Always do your fair share of the work, even if you don't agree with all the decisions made by your team. Tell people promptly if you are having problems so there is time to solve them. Be loyal to your team when you're talking to other people.

Being the team leader

It can be difficult to strike a balance between 'leading' the team and working with friends. You need to inspire and motivate your team without being bossy or critical.

Important points to remember about being a team leader

- Lead by example. Stay pleasant, consistent and control your temper, even under pressure.
- Everyone is different. Your ways of working may not always be the best.
- Be prepared to listen and contribute positively to a discussion.
- Encourage quieter team members to join in discussions by asking for their views.
- Be prepared to do whatever you ask other people to do.
- Note down what you say you will do, so that you don't forget.
- Discuss alternatives with people rather than giving orders.
- Be sensitive to other people's feelings. They may have personal problems or issues that affect their behaviour.
- Learn the art of persuasion.
- Act as peacemaker. Help people reach a compromise when necessary.
- Give team members the credit for their hard work or good ideas.
- Admit your mistakes. Look for a positive solution and think about what can be learned for the future, rather than making excuses.
- Praise and encourage team members who are working hard.
- Make criticisms constructively, and in private.
- Be assertive (put forward your point of view firmly) rather than aggressive (attacking other people to defend yourself.)

Some notes of caution about being a team leader

- Try to look pleasant and don't glare at people who interrupt you unexpectedly.
- Never talk about team members behind their backs.
- Don't gossip, exaggerate to make a point, spread rumours, speculate or tell lies.
- Don't expect to get your own way all the time – all good leaders back down on occasion.
- Never criticise any colleagues in front of other people. Speak to them in private and keep it constructive.

TOP TIP

Excellent ideas often come from quiet team members. Encourage everyone to make suggestions so that you don't overlook any valuable contributions.

Key points

- There are many benefits of working in a group or as a team. These include mutual support, companionship and the exchange of ideas.
- You will be expected to work co-operatively with other people at work, and during many course assignments.
- It isn't easy learning to be a team leader. Team leaders should be fair, consistent and pleasant to work with, as well as loyal and sensitive to the needs of team members.

Action points

1 Identify the role of teamwork in your area of study. Identify the team's goal and any factors you think will contribute towards its success.

2 Decide how you would handle each of the following difficult situations if you were the team leader. If you can, discuss your ideas with a friend in your class.
   a) The team needs to borrow a college video camera to record an event being held tonight. Your tutor tells you that the one you reserved last week is not working and the rest are out on loan.
   b) A member of your team has personal problems so you have given him less work to do. Now you've been accused of having favourites.
   c) A team member is constantly letting everyone down because of poor work and non-attendance at group meetings.
   d) Two team members have disagreed about how to do a task. You're not bothered how they do it as long as it gets done properly, and by the deadline.
   e) A team member becomes very aggressive whenever she is challenged in any way – no matter how mildly.

3 Identify someone who has inspired you because they've been an excellent leader. This could be someone you've met, a fictional character or a famous person. Note down what it is about them that impressed you.

Activity: Observing behaviour

Observe a conversation between two people. This could be done in a care setting between a carer and a client or in a public situation such as a coffee shop or bus stop.

You don't need to hear the conversation to complete this activity. Just observe the people's body language.

Use the following chart to record your findings.

Behaviour observed	Person one	Person two
Interruptions from the listener		
How the two are sitting e.g. *facing each other, beside each other, next to each other*		
The way they are positioned e.g. *leaning towards each other, holding hands, crossed legs/arms*		
Who talks most		
Fidgeting e.g. *tapping foot, jiggling leg, playing with hair*		
Eye contact		
Signs of boredom e.g. *looking away, tapping table, fidgeting*		
Environmental obstructions e.g. *tables in the way, books used to hide behind, tall furniture blocking view*		

Below is an example of how you could fill it in.

Behaviour observed.	Person one	Person two
Eye contact	Held eye contact with person two throughout the conversation.	Kept looking away all the time. Did not maintain eye contact.
Fidgeting	Sat very still, in fact she sat on her hands for the whole conversation.	Kept tapping the table with her pen.

How could your findings be used to help others understand how they might work in a group or as part of a team?

Did you find some things that would prevent a team working well? For example, who talked most? Did one person dominate the conversation?

Step Eight: Understand how to research and analyse information

Case study: Researching information

Class A of the BTEC National Diploma in Health and Social Care are due to undertake some primary research for Unit 22: Research Methodology for Health and Social Care. The class must devise a questionnaire to ask other learners in the centre about a relevant health issue. The class is then spilt into small groups.

Group A consists of three popular boys aged 18. Group B consists of two women in their 20s, both of whom have children in the centre's nursery. Group C consists of four very outgoing and confident girls aged 17. The class spend a lesson preparing a questionnaire about teenage use and knowledge of contraception. All three groups take a copy of the same questionnaire around the centre asking about 20 learners for their views and opinions.

Group A, the boys, took their questionnaire to the beauty therapy department. They were surprised that very few of the learners knew about contraception and several refused to answer their questions at all.

Group B got good results from a variety of learners from all around the centre. They asked males and females of a variety of different ages and from a variety of different courses.

Group C, the girls, went to the sports department and found that learners only knew about using condoms.

Each group was asked to analyse their findings and present their results to the rest of the class. All three groups were surprised to discover that they had very different results to their questionnaires even though they had all asked the same questions.

Reflection points

Who do you think got the most accurate results? Why is that?

Think about how you research information. Are your current techniques effective?

As a BTEC Level 3 National learner, you often have to find information for yourself. This skill will be invaluable in your working life, and if you continue your studies at higher education (HE) level. Sometimes the information will give you a better understanding of a topic, at other times you will research to obtain information for a project or assignment. Sometimes you may be so interested in something that you want to find out more without being told to do so!

Whatever your reason, and no matter where your information can be found, there is a good and not so good way to go about the task. This section will help if you can't find what you want, or find too much, or drift aimlessly around a library, or watch a demonstration and don't know what to ask afterwards.

Types of information

There are many types of information and many different sources. Depending on the task, these are the sources you may need to consult.

- **Verbal information.** This includes talking to friends, colleagues at work, members of your family, listening to experts explain what they do, interviewing people, talking to sales reps at an exhibition or customers about a product.

- **Printed information**. This includes information printed in newspapers, journals, magazines, books, posters, workshop manuals, leaflets and catalogues. The type of magazine or newspaper you read may have its own slant on the information, which you may have to take into account (see page 59).

- **Written information**. This includes course notes and handouts, reports and other documents in the workplace. If you want to use written information from work, you must check this is allowed, and that it doesn't contain confidential material such as financial information or staff names and addresses.

- **Graphical information.** This includes illustrations, pictures, cartoons, line drawings, graphs and photographs. Graphics can make something clearer than words alone. For example, a satnav instruction book might contain illustrations to show different procedures.

- **Electronic information.** This includes information from electronic sources such as DVDs, CD-ROMs, searchable databases, websites, podcasts, webinars (**seminars** online), emails and text messages. The huge amount of information available online is both a help and a hindrance. You can find information quickly, but the source may be unreliable, out-of-date, inaccurate or inappropriate (see page 58.)

TOP TIP

Too much information is as bad as too little, because it's overwhelming. The trick is to find good quality, relevant information and know when to call a halt to your search.

TOP TIP

Consider all appropriate sources and don't just rely on information found online.

Finding what you need

Spend a few minutes planning what to do before you start looking for information. This can save a lot of time later on.

The following steps will help you to do this.

1 Make sure you understand exactly what it is you need to know so that you don't waste time looking for the wrong thing.

2 Clarify your objectives to narrow down your search. Think about why the information is wanted and how much detail you need. For example, learners studying BTEC Nationals in Engineering and Performing Arts may both be researching 'noise' for their projects but they are likely to need different types of information and use it in different ways.

3 Identify your sources and check you know how to use them. You need to choose sources that are most likely to provide information relevant to your objectives. For example, an Engineering learner might find information on noise emissions in industry journals and by checking out specialist websites.

4 Plan and schedule your research. Theoretically, you could research information forever. Knowing when to call a halt takes skill. Write a schedule that states when you must stop looking and start sorting the information.

5 Store your information safely in a labelled folder. This folder should include printouts or photocopies of articles, notes about events you have attended or observed, photographs you've taken or sketches you've drawn. Divide your information under topic headings to make it easier to find. When you're ready to start work, re-read your assignment brief and select the items that are most closely related to the task you are doing.

TOP TIP

Allocate time for research as part of your assignment task. Take into account any interim deadlines as well as the final deadline for completing the work.

Primary and secondary research, and the law of copyright

There are two ways to research information. One is known as primary research, the other is secondary research.

Primary research

Primary research involves finding new information about an issue or topic. This might include finding out people's views about a product or interviewing an expert. When carrying out interviews, you will need to design a survey or questionnaire. Your primary research might also include observing or experiencing something for yourself, and recording your feelings and observations.

Secondary research

Secondary research involves accessing information that already exists in books, files, newspapers or on CD-ROMs, computer databases or the internet, and assessing it against your objectives.

This information has been prepared by other people and is available to anyone. You can quote from an original work provided you acknowledge the source of your information. You should put this acknowledgement in your text or in the bibliography to your text; do not claim it as your own research. You must include the author's name, year of publication, the title and publisher, or the web address if it is an online article. You should practise listing the sources of articles so

that you feel confident writing a bibliography. Use the guidance sheet issued by your centre to help you. This will illustrate the style your centre recommends.

The trick with research is to choose the best technique to achieve your objectives and this may mean using a mix of methods and resources. For example, if you have to comment on an industry event you might go to it, make notes, interview people attending, observe the event (perhaps take a video camera), and read any newspaper reports or online comments.

TOP TIP

Always make sure you make a note of where you get information from (your source). Keep it safely as it can be very difficult later on to work out where it came from!

People as a source of information

If you want to get the most out of interviewing someone, or several people, you need to prepare carefully in advance.

The following points give some general advice about getting the most out of face-to-face interviews.

- Make sure you know what questions to ask to get the information you need.
- Explain why you want the information.
- Don't expect to be told confidential or sensitive information.
- Write clear notes so that you remember who told you what, and when. (See also page 60.)
- Note the contact details of the person you are interviewing and ask whether they mind if you contact them again should you think of anything later or need to clarify your notes.
- Thank them for their help.

If you want to ask a lot of people for their opinion you may want to conduct a survey. You will need to design a questionnaire and analyse the results. This will be easier if you ask for **quantitative** responses – for example yes/no, true/false or ratings on a five-point scale – rather than opinions.

- Give careful thought to your representative sample (people whose opinions are relevant to the topic.)
- Decide how many people to survey so that the results mean something.
- Keep the survey relatively short.
- Thank people who complete it.
- Analyse the results, and write up your conclusions promptly.

TOP TIP

Test your questionnaire on volunteers before you 'go live' to check that there are no mistakes and the questions are easy to understand. Make any amendments before you conduct your 'real' survey.

Asking someone who knows a lot about a topic can be informative.

Avoiding pitfalls

Wikipedia is a good online source that covers many topics, and often in some depth. It is popular and free. However, it has an open-content policy, which means that anyone can contribute to and edit entries. People may post information, whether it is correct or not. Wikipedia is moving towards greater checks on entries, but it is still sensible to check out information you find on this site somewhere else.

Apart from inaccuracy, there are other problems that you may find with any information you obtain through research, especially material found online.

- **Out-of-date material.** Check the date of everything and keep only the latest version of books, newspapers or magazines. Yesterday's news may be of little use if you are researching something topical.
- **Irrelevant details.** Often, only part of an article will be relevant to your search. For example, if you are forecasting future trends in an area of work, you do not need information about its history or related problems. When learners are struggling, they sometimes 'pad out' answers with irrelevant information. If you've researched properly you can avoid this by having enough relevant information for your purposes.

- **Invalid assumptions.** This means someone has jumped to the wrong conclusion and made 2 + 2 = 5. You might do this if you see two friends chatting and think they are talking about you – whether they are or not! You can avoid problems in this area by double-checking your ideas and getting evidence to support them.

- **Bias.** This is when people hold strong views about a topic, or let their emotions or prejudices affect their judgement. An obvious example is asking a keen football fan for an objective evaluation of their team's performance!

- **Vested interests.** People may argue in a certain way because it's in their own interests to do so. For example, when the Government said Home Information Packs must be prepared for all properties being sold, the Association of Home Information Pack Providers was in favour because it trains the people who prepare the packs. The National Association of Estate Agents and Royal Institution of Chartered Surveyors were not because they thought they would lose business if people were put off selling their houses.

TOP TIP

Don't discard information that is affected by bias or vested interests. Just make it clear you know about the problem and have taken it into account.

Reading for a purpose

You may enjoy reading or you may find it tedious or difficult. If so, it helps to know that there are different ways to read, depending on what you're doing. For example, you wouldn't look for a programme in a TV guide in the same way that you would check an assignment for mistakes. You can save time and find information more easily if you use the best method of reading to suit your purpose. The following are some examples of ways of reading.

- **Skim reading** is used to check new information and get a general overview.
To skim a book chapter read the first and last paragraphs, the headings, subheadings and illustrations. It also helps to read the first sentence of each paragraph.

TOP TIP

News articles are written with the key points at the beginning, so concentrate on the first paragraph or two. Feature articles have a general introduction and important information is contained in the main text.

- **Scanning** is used to see whether an article contains something you need – such as key words, dates or technical terms.
Focus on capital or initial letters for a name, and figures for a date. Technical terms may be in bold or italics.

- **Light reading** is usually done for pleasure when you are relaxed, for example, reading a magazine article. You may not remember many facts afterwards, so this sort of reading isn't suitable for learning something or assessing its value.

- **Word-by-word reading (proofreading)** is important so that you don't miss anything, such as the dosage instructions for a strong medicine. You should proofread assignments before you submit them.

- **Reading for study (active reading)** means being actively involved so that you understand the information. It is rare to be naturally good at this, so you might have to work to develop this skill.

Developing critical and analytical skills

Developing critical and analytical skills involves looking at information for any flaws in the arguments. These skills are important when you progress to work or higher education (HE), so it's useful to practise them now on your BTEC Level 3 National course.

A useful technique for understanding, analysing, evaluating and remembering what you are reading is **SQ4R**.

SQ4R is an effective method. It consists of six steps.

1 Survey first, to get a general impression. Scan the information to see what it is about, when it was written and by whom. The source, and the reason it was written, may be important. Most newspapers, for example, have their own 'slant' that affects how information is presented.

2 Question your aims for reading this material. What are you hoping to find? What questions are you expecting it to answer?

3 Read the information three or four times. The first time, aim to get a general idea of the content. Use a dictionary to look up any new words. Then read more carefully to really understand what the writer means.

4 Respond by thinking critically about the information and how it relates to the topic you are studying. Does it answer your queries partially, fully or not at all? What information is factual and what is based on opinion? Is there evidence to support these opinions? Is there a reason why the author has taken this standpoint? Do you agree with it? How does it link to other information you have read? What is the opposite argument and is there any evidence to support this? Overall, how useful is this information?

5 Record the information by noting the key points. Use this to refresh your memory, if necessary, rather than re-reading the article.

6 Review your notes against the original to check you have included all important points. If you are also preparing a presentation, reviewing your notes will help you to remember key points more easily.

TOP TIP

SQ4R is just one method of reading for study. Research others and adapt them to suit your own style.

Taking good notes

There are many occasions when you need to take notes, such as when a visiting speaker is talking to your class. There's no point taking notes unless you write them in a way that will allow you to use them later.

Note-taking is a personal activity. Some people prefer to make diagrammatical sketches with key points in boxes linked by arrows; others prefer to write a series of bullet points. You will develop your own style, but the following hints and tips might help you at the start.

- Use A4 lined paper, rather than a notebook, so that you have more space and don't need to turn over so often.
- When you're reading for study, make sure you have a dictionary, pen, notepad and highlighter to hand.
- Leave a wide margin to record your own comments or queries.
- Put a heading at the top, such as the speaker's name and topic, as well as the date.
- If you are making notes from a book or an article, remember SQ4R and read it several times first. Your notes will only be effective if you understand the information.
- Don't write in complete sentences – it takes too long.
- Leave spaces for later additions or corrections.
- Use headings to keep your notes clear and well organised.
- Only write down relevant information, including key words and phrases.

- Highlight, underline or use capitals for essential points.
- Never copy chunks of text – always use your own words.
- Clearly identify quotations, and record your sources, so that you can cite them in your work. (Note the author's name, title, publisher, date and place of publication and the page number.)

TOP TIP

Make sure your information is accurate, up-to-date, relevant and valid. Be aware of bias, and don't confuse fact with opinion.

Key points

- Useful information may be verbal, printed, written, graphical or electronic.
- Effective research means knowing exactly what you are trying to find and where to look. Know how reference media are stored in your library and how to search online. Store important information carefully.
- Primary research is original data you obtain yourself. Secondary research is information prepared by someone else. If you use this, you must quote your sources in a bibliography.
- You can search for information by skimming and scanning, and read in different ways. Reading for study means actively involving yourself with the text, questioning what you are reading and making notes to help your own understanding.
- Read widely around a topic to get different viewpoints. Don't accept everything you read as correct. Think about how it fits with other information you have obtained.
- Taking notes is a personal skill that takes time to develop. Start by using A4 lined pages with a margin, set out your notes clearly and label them. Only record essential information.

Action points

- Working with a friend, look back at the sources of information listed on page 56. For each type, identify examples of information relevant to your course that you could obtain from each source. See how many you can list under each type.
- Check your ability to find the information you need by answering each of the questions in **Activity: Finding information** on the next page. For any questions you get wrong, your first research task is to find out the correct answers as quickly as you can.
- Go to page 88 to find out how to access a website where you can check your ability to skim and scan information, improve your ability to differentiate fact from opinion, summarise text and much more.
- Check your ability to sort fact from opinion and spot vested interests by completing **Activity: Let's give you a tip...** on page 64. Check your ideas with the answers on page 87.

TOP TIP

Make a note of any information that you are struggling to understand so that you can discuss it with your tutor.

Activity: Finding information

Answer the following questions about finding information.

a) Four types of information that are available from the library in your centre, besides books, are:

1

2

3

4

b) When I visit the library, the way to check if a book I want is available is:

c) The difference between borrowing a book on short-term loan and on long-term loan is:

Short-term loan:

Long-term loan:

d) The journals that are stocked by the library that are relevant to my course include:

e) Useful information on the intranet at my centre includes:

f) Searchable databases and online magazines I can access include:

g) The quickest way to check if a book or journal contains the type of information I need is to:

h) The difference between a search engine, a portal, a directory site and a forum is:

i) Bookmarking useful websites means:

j) In addition to suggesting websites, Google can also provide the following types of information:

k) Specialist websites which provide useful information related to my course include:

l) Useful tips I would give to people starting on my course who need to find out information are:

Activity: Let's give you a tip...

In 2009, many businesses were struggling thanks to the credit crunch and falling consumer demand. Some, like Woolworths, closed down altogether. Others laid off staff, or announced wage cuts. Despite this, the Government approved recommendations by the Low Pay Commission to increase the minimum wage rate from October. Although the rise was only small, many unions, including Unison and Usdaw, agreed it was better than a freeze, which had been wanted by the British Chambers of Commerce and the British Retail Consortium.

The Government also announced new laws to stop restaurants and bars using tips to top up staff pay to the minimum level. *The Independent* newspaper claimed its 'fair tips, fair pay' campaign had won the day. It also reported that the British Hospitality Association was claiming this could result in up to 45,000 job losses. The Unite union also carried out a campaign and its General Secretary claimed the decision a triumph for the poorly paid. Not everyone agreed. Some thought there should be no tipping at all, as in Australia. Others said the Canadian system was best – wages are low but generous tips are left, and this motivates staff to give excellent service.

a) Look at the table below. In your view, which of the statements are facts and which are opinions? In each case, justify your view.

Statement	Fact or opinion?	Justification
i) Having a national minimum wage helps low-paid workers.		
ii) Over one million people will benefit from the minimum wage increase.		
iii) The new law on tips will stop restaurants paying below minimum wage rates.		
iv) Using the Australian system of no tips would be better.		
v) The Canadian system guarantees good service.		
vi) 45,000 job losses will occur in the hospitality industry.		

b) All newspapers have their own way of putting forward the news. Go to page 88 to find out how you can access a website which will help you to compare the way that news is reported in different newspapers.

Compare six different newspapers and make notes on:
i) the type of stories covered

ii) the way views are put forward.

Activity: How to go about your research

Look carefully at the case study at the beginning of this section.

1 Were the researchers biased in their approach? If so, how?

2 Look at the following ethical considerations. How should they be applied to a questionnaire asking young people about their use of contraception?

- Confidentiality

- Informed consent

- Do no harm to participant

- Right to withdraw their participation

- Debriefing about results of research

On the day, you can achieve a better performance if you:

- arrive in plenty of time
- calm your nerves by taking deep breaths before going in front of your audience
- introduce yourself clearly, and smile at the audience
- avoid reading from your screen or your notes
- explain what you are going to do – especially if giving a demonstration – do it and then review what you've done
- say you will deal with questions at the end of any demonstration
- answer questions honestly – don't exaggerate, guess or waffle
- respond positively to all feedback, which should be used to improve your performance next time.

TOP TIPS

Make sure you can be heard clearly by lifting your head and speaking a little more slowly and loudly than normal.

Key points

- When making a presentation, prepare well, don't be too ambitious and have several rehearsals.
- When giving a demonstration, explain first what you are going to do and that you will answer questions at the end.

Case study: Learner quotes about making presentations

Most people start off feeling uncomfortable about talking in front of a group of people, whether you know them or not. This is what some real learners have said about having to give presentations as part of their BTEC course.

"I actually feel more comfortable giving a presentation rather than having to write an essay. What I really enjoy about it is the fact that sometimes we have to prepare a presentation as a whole group. I like that we work together to find information and then we take turns presenting different points. The fact that I am not the only one out there and I am part of a supportive team makes it fun for me."

Gabriela, 16, BTEC Level 2 First in Performing Arts

"Although presentations are very stressful, when I present my work it helps to hang my ideas together and I find I can express what I want to say more clearly than when I write things down. Instant feedback is helpful and boosts my confidence for the next time."

Ethan, 19, BTEC Level 2 First in Creative Media Production

"I think presentations are useful but I find them difficult to deliver – relying heavily on my memory, which is very nerve-racking. We were told that presentation would be part of our assessment. I really worried about it and couldn't sleep the night before – stressing out about what I was going to say. I hated the first few minutes, but after that I was OK."

Will, 16, BTEC Level 2 First in Engineering

"I was very nervous about presenting to my class until I took part in the Young Enterprise scheme and had to present the results of our project to over 200 people including the mayor! After that presenting to my class mates didn't feel too nerve wracking at all."

Lizzy, 17, BTEC Level 2 First in Business

"I used to dread presentations on my course, but found that if I went through my notes again and again until I knew the presentation inside out, it made it much easier and the presentations generally went well."

Javinder, 17, BTEC Level 3 National in Construction

Activity: All right on the night?

Read the following account and answer the questions that follow. If possible, compare ideas with a friend in your class.

Gemma looked around in exasperation. The team were on the final rehearsal of their presentation and nothing was going right. Amaya seemed to think it was funny. 'Honestly, Gemma, why don't you just chill for a bit?' she suggested. 'You know what they say – a bad dress rehearsal means we'll do really well tomorrow!'

Gemma glared at her. 'Well, can I make a suggestion, too, Amaya,' she retorted. 'Why don't you just concentrate for a change? Sprawling around and dissolving into giggles every five minutes isn't helping either.'

She turned to Adam. 'And I thought you were going to build a simple model,' she said, 'not one that falls apart every time you touch it.'

Adam looked crest-fallen. 'But I wanted to show how it worked.'

'How it's supposed to work, you mean!' raged Gemma, all her worries and anxieties now coming to the fore. 'We'll look stupid if it ends up in bits on the floor tomorrow and Amaya just falls about laughing again.'

'And Imran,' continued Gemma, turning her sights on the last member of the team, 'why is it so difficult for you to count to three minutes? We've agreed over and over again we'll each talk for three minutes and every time you get carried away with the sound of your own voice and talk for twice as long. It just means we're going to overrun and get penalised. And stop trying to wriggle out of answering questions properly. For heaven's sake, if you don't know the answer, how hard is it just to say so?'

Silence fell. No-one looked at each other. Adam fiddled with his model and something else fell off. Amaya wanted to laugh but didn't dare.

Imran was sulking and vowed never to say anything ever again. 'You wait,' he thought. 'Tomorrow I'll race through my part in one minute flat. And then what are you going to do?'

1 Identify the strengths and weaknesses of each member of the presentation team.

Name	Strengths	Weaknesses
Gemma		
Amaya		
Adam		
Imran		

2 What have the team done right, so far, in getting ready for their presentation?

3 Why do you think they are having problems?

4 If you were Gemma's tutor, what advice would you give her at this point?

Activity: Preparing your presentation

Complete the following plan before you do a presentation for one of your assignments.

Title of presentation ....

Date of presentation ....

Time of presentation ....

Length of presentation ....

Room for presentation ....

Number of people watching presentation ....

Type of presentation ....

Activity	Resources needed	Tick when completed
Research information for presentation		
Write notes and draft presentation		
Practise presentation, reading it aloud to yourself or one other person		
Amend draft notes		
Write up final notes		
Practise presentation again		
Make any final changes		

You could consider adding pictures, music, sound or video clips and class participation to your presentation, to make it more interesting. If every member of the class is doing a PowerPoint presentation on the same subject, how are you going to make yours more interesting and different from theirs? Think about other methods of presenting a subject other than PowerPoint.

For example, to demonstrate how the heart works, you could give each member of the class a piece of a puzzle that makes a large paper heart if put together in the right order. They could stick their pieces on the board with your help. This way you have demonstrated that you understand how the heart works but have tried something other than PowerPoint. Which would be more fun and memorable?

Step Ten: Maximise your opportunities and manage your problems

Case study: Managing your problems

Raj thinks he wants to be a mental health nurse when he has finished his BTEC National Subsidiary Diploma in Health and Social Care. His birthday is in August, so he will not be 18 before he finishes the course. Consequently he will not have the opportunity to work with any adults with mental health problems while on the course. Raj wants to maximise his potential, ensuring that when he applies to go into nursing he has as much knowledge and experience as possible.

To do this Raj volunteers to work in a school for children with behavioural problems. He helps out at the school for one afternoon a week when he isn't at the centre. He also subscribes to a mental health journal, which helps him keep up to date with current mental health issues. Raj's mother listens to Radio 4 a lot, which often presents case studies about

people living with mental health problems. She suggests that Raj listens to the podcasts from the radio shows in the evenings when everyone else is busy. Raj's father reads several daily newspapers and enjoys cutting out relevant reports for Raj to read.

Raj is thankful for the support his family is offering him, but wishes that he could gain some practical experience to see if mental health is a field he really wants to go into.

Reflection points

Can you think of any ways Raj could get mental health experience?

What would you do to ensure that you have knowledge and experience before applying to go into nursing?

If your course takes one or two years to complete, then it is highly likely that you will experience some highs and lows in that time. You may find one or two topics harder than the rest. There may be distractions in your personal life to cope with. All of which means than you may not always be able to do your best.

It is, therefore, sensible to have an action plan to help you cope. It's also wise to plan how to make the best of opportunities for additional experiences or learning. This section shows you how to do this.

TOP TIP

Because life rarely runs smoothly, it's sensible to capitalise on the opportunities that come your way and have a plan to deal with problems.

Making the most of your opportunities

There will be many opportunities for learning on your course, not all of which will be in school or college. You should prepare for some of the following to maximise the opportunities that each offer.

- **External visits**. Prepare in advance by reading about relevant topics. Make notes when you are there. Write up your notes neatly and file them safely for future reference.

- **Visiting speakers**. Questions can usually be submitted to the speaker in advance. Think carefully about information that you would find helpful. Make notes, unless someone has been appointed to make notes for the whole group. You may be asked to thank the speaker on behalf of your group.

- **Work experience**. If work experience is an essential part of your course, your tutor will help you to organise your placement and tell you about the evidence you need to obtain. You may also get a special logbook in which to record your experiences. Read and re-read the units to which your evidence will apply and make sure you understand the grading criteria and what you need to obtain. Make time to write up your notes, logbook and/or diary every night (if possible), while everything is fresh in your mind.

- **In your own workplace**. If you have a full-time or part-time job, watch for opportunities to find out more about relevant topics that relate to your course, such as health and safety, teamwork, dealing with customers, IT security and communications. Your employer will have had to address all of these issues. Finding out more about these issues will broaden your knowledge and give more depth to your assessment responses.

- **Television, newspapers, podcasts and other information sources**. The media can be an invaluable source of information. Look out for news bulletins relating to your studies, as well as information in topical television programmes – from *The Apprentice* to *Top Gear*. You can also read news headlines online (see page 88). Podcasts are useful, too. It will help if you know what topics you will be studying in the months to come, so you can spot useful opportunities as they arise.

TOP TIP

Remember that you can use online catch-up services, such as the BBC iPlayer or 4oD (for Channel 4 shows) to see TV programmes you have missed recently.

Minimising problems

Hopefully, any problems you experience during your course will only be minor; such as struggling to find an acceptable working method with someone in your team.

You should already know who to talk to about these issues, and who to go to if that person is absent or you would prefer to talk to someone else. If your problems are affecting your work, it's sensible to see your tutor promptly. It is a rare learner who is enthusiastic about every topic and gets on well with everyone else doing the course, so your tutor won't be surprised and will give you useful guidance (in confidence) to help.

TOP TIP

Don't delay talking to someone in confidence if you have a serious problem. If your course tutor is unavailable, talk to another staff member you like and trust instead.

Other sources of help

If you are unfortunate enough to have a more serious personal problem, the following sources of help may be available in your centre.

- **Professional counselling.** There may be a professional counselling service. If you see a counsellor, nothing you say during the session can be mentioned to another member of staff without your permission.
- **Complaint procedures.** If you have a serious complaint, the first step is to talk to your tutor. If you can't resolve your problem informally, there will be a formal learner complaint procedure. These procedures are used only for serious issues, not for minor difficulties.
- **Appeals procedures.** If you disagree with your final grade for an assignment, check the grading criteria and ask the subject tutor to explain how the grade was awarded. If you are still unhappy, talk to your personal tutor. If you still disagree, you have the right to make a formal appeal.
- **Disciplinary procedures.** These exist for when learners consistently flout a centre's rules and ensure that all learners are dealt with in the same way. Hopefully, you will never get into trouble, but you should make sure that you read these procedures carefully to see what could happen if you did. Remember that being honest and making a swift apology is always the wisest course of action.
- **Serious illness.** Whether this involves you, a family member or a close friend, it could affect your attendance. Discuss the problem with your tutor promptly; you will be missing information from the first day you are absent. There are many solutions in this type of situation – such as sending notes by post and updating you electronically (providing you are well enough to cope with the work.)

Key points

- Don't miss opportunities to learn more about relevant topics through external visits, listening to visiting speakers, work experience, being at work or even watching television.
- If you have difficulties or concerns, talk to your tutor, or another appropriate person, promptly to make sure your work isn't affected.

Action points

1 Prepare in advance to maximise your opportunities.
   a) List the opportunities available on your course for obtaining more information and talking to experts. You can check with your tutor to make sure you've identified them all.
   b) Check the content of each unit you will be studying so that you know the main topics and focus of each.
   c) Identify the information that may be relevant to your course on television, on radio, in newspapers and in podcasts.

2 Make sure you know how to cope if you have a serious problem.
   a) Check your centre's procedures so you know who to talk to in a crisis, and who to contact if that person is absent.
   b) Find out where you can get hold of a copy of the main procedures in your centre that might affect you if you have a serious problem. Then read them.

Activity: Maximising your potential

There are many different ways to maximise your potential. Look at the following scenarios and solutions and try to match them together. Draw a line between the boxes matching the scenario with the possible resource. Remember there may be more than one answer for each scenario.

Scenarios	Resources
Jack wants to be an ambulance technician	Undertake a First Aid course
Sally doesn't know what career she wants to go into.	Talk to a counsellor
Tina is doing very well on her course – better than she expected	Talk to a Careers Advisor
Sheena is concerned that she is failing her course	Volunteer to read to children in a school
Josh doesn't know what jobs are available after his course	Read the local papers.
Morwena wants to work with children	Find a healthcare job for the weekends.
	Talk to tutor or teacher for advice

TOP TIP

The time and effort you will be putting into this course deserves to be rewarded. Make sure you know how to confront and successfully overcome problems.

AND FINALLY ...

Refer to this Study Skills Guide whenever you need to remind yourself about something related to your course. Keep it in a safe place so that you can use it whenever you need to refresh your memory. That way, you'll get the very best out of your course – and yourself!

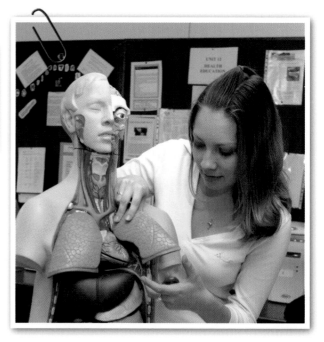

Your Study Skills Guide will help you gain the skills you need for success.

Skills building

This section has been written to help you improve the skills needed to do your best in your assignments. You may be excellent at some skills already, others may need further work. The skills you can expect to demonstrate on your course include:

- your personal, learning and thinking skills (**PLTS**)
- your **functional skills** of ICT, maths/numeracy and English
- your proofreading and document production skills.

Personal, learning and thinking skills (PLTS)

These are the skills, personal qualities and behaviour that enable you to operate more independently, work more confidently with other people and be more effective at work. You'll develop these on your BTEC Level 3 National course through a variety of experiences and as you take on different roles and responsibilities.

The skills are divided into six groups:

1 **Independent enquirers** can process and evaluate information they investigate from different perspectives. They can plan what to do and how to do it, and take into account the consequences of making different decisions.

2 **Creative thinkers** generate and explore different ideas. They make connections between ideas, events and experiences that enable them to be inventive and imaginative.

3 **Reflective learners** can assess themselves and other people. They can evaluate their own strengths and limitations. They set themselves realistic goals, monitor their own performance and welcome feedback.

4 **Team workers** collaborate with other people to achieve common goals. They are fair and considerate to others, whether as a team leader or team member, and take account of different opinions.

5 **Self-managers** are well-organised and show personal responsibility, initiative, creativity and enterprise. They look for new challenges and responsibilities and are flexible when priorities change.

6 **Effective participators** play a full part in the life of their school, college, workplace or wider community by taking responsible action to bring improvements for others as well as themselves.

Action points

1 Many parts of this Study Skills Guide relate to the development of your own personal, learning and thinking skills. For each of the following, suggest the main skill groups to which the chapter relates. Refer to the box above and write a number next to each chapter title below.

a) Use your time wisely. ____

b) Understand how to research and analyse information. ____

c) Work productively as a member of a group. ____

d) Understand yourself. ____

e) Utilise all your resources. ____

f) Maximise your opportunities and manage your problems. ____

2 You have been on your BTEC National course for a few months now and, although everyone is enjoying the work, you realise that some of the learners have complaints.

Firstly, several learners object to an increase in the price of printouts and photocopying, on the basis that they can't do good work for their assignments if this is too expensive. You disagree and think that the prices are reasonable, given the cost of paper.

Secondly, a timetable change means your 2 pm – 4 pm Friday afternoon class has been moved to 9 am – 11 am. Some learners are annoyed and want it changed back, while others are delighted.

a) For the first problem, identify four factors which could indicate that those complaining about the price rise might be justified.

1

2

3

4

b) For the second problem:

i) Think about which learners in your group would be most affected by the timetable change. Who might be most disturbed? Who might benefit from the earlier start?

ii) Try to think of a creative solution, or compromise, that would please both groups.

c) During the discussions about these issues, some quieter members of the class are often shouted down by the more excitable members. Suggest a strategy for dealing with this, which everyone is likely to accept.

You can also check your ideas with the suggestions given on page 87.

3 a) Complete the chart opposite, identifying occasions when you may need to demonstrate personal, learning and thinking skills in your future career. Alternatively, apply each area to a part-time job you are currently doing.

b) Identify areas where you think you are quite strong and put a tick in the 'S' column. Check that you could provide evidence to support this judgement, such as a time when you have demonstrated this skill.

c) Now consider areas where you are not so good and put a cross in the 'W' column.

d) Then practise self-management by identifying two appropriate goals to achieve over the next month and make a note of them in the space provided. If possible, talk through your ideas at your next individual tutorial.

Personal, learning and thinking skills for future career/current part-time job				
Skill group	**Example skills**	**Occasions when you use/ will use skill**	**S**	**W**
Independent enquirers	Finding information Solving problems Making decisions Reconciling conflicting information or views Justifying decisions			
Creative thinkers	Finding imaginative solutions Making original connections Finding new ways to do something Opportunities for being innovative and inventive			
Reflective learners	Goals you may set yourself Reviewing your own progress Encouraging feedback Dealing with setbacks or criticism			
Team workers	Working with others Coping with different views to your own Adapting your behaviour Being fair and considerate			
Self-managers	Being self-starting and showing initiative Dealing positively with changing priorities Organising your own time and resources Dealing with pressure Managing your emotions			
Effective participators	Identifying issues of concern to others Proposing ways forward Identifying improvements for others Influencing other people Putting forward a persuasive argument			
Goals	1			
	2			

Functional skills

Functional skills are practical skills that everyone needs to have in order to study and work effectively. They involve using and applying English, maths and ICT.

Improving your literacy skills

Your written English communication skills

A good vocabulary increases your ability to explain yourself clearly. Work that is presented without spelling and punctuation errors looks professional, and increases the likelihood of someone understanding your intended meaning. Your written communication skills will be tested in many assignments. You should work at improving areas of weakness, such as spelling, punctuation or vocabulary.

Try the following to help you improve your written communication skills:

- Read more as this introduces you to new words, and it will help your spelling.
- Look up new words in a dictionary and try to use them in conversation.
- Use a Thesaurus (you can access one electronically in Word) to find alternatives to words you use a lot, this adds variety to your work.
- Never use words you don't understand in the hope that they sound impressive.
- Write neatly, so people can read what you've written.
- Do crosswords to improve your word power and spelling.
- Improve your punctuation – especially the use of apostrophes – either by using an online programme or by using a communication textbook.
- Go to page 88 to find out how to gain access to some helpful websites for this page.

Verbal and non-verbal communication (NVC) skills

Talking appropriately means using the right words and 'tone'; using the right body language means sending positive signals to reinforce this message – such as smiling at someone when you say 'Hello'. Both verbal and non-verbal communication skills are essential when dealing with people at work.

The following are some hints for successful communication:

- Be polite, tactful and sensitive to other people's feelings.
- Think about the words and phrases that you like to hear, and use them when communicating with other people.
- Use simple language so that people can understand you easily. Explain what you mean, when necessary.
- Speak at the right pace. Don't speak so slowly that everyone loses interest, or so fast that no-one can understand you.
- Speak loudly enough for people to hear you clearly – but don't shout!
- Think about the specific needs of different people – whether you are talking to a senior manager, an important client, a shy colleague or an angry customer.
- Recognise the importance of non-verbal communication (NVC) so that you send positive signals by smiling, making eye contact, giving an encouraging nod or leaning forwards to show interest.
- Read other people's body language to spot if they are anxious or impatient so that you can react appropriately.

TOP TIP

Make sure you use the right tone for the person you're talking to. Would you talk to an adult in the same way you'd talk to a very young child?

Action points

1 Go to page 88 to find out how to gain access to websites which can help you to improve your literacy skills.

2 A battery made in China contained the following information.

> ### DO NOT CONNECT IMPROPERLY
> ### CHARGE OR DISPOSE OF IN FIRE

a) Can you see any problems with this? Give a reason for your answer.

b) Reword the information so that it is unambiguous.

3 If you ever thought you could completely trust the spellchecker on your computer, type the text given in box A on the next page into your computer. Your spellchecker will not highlight a single error; yet even at a glance you should be able to spot dozens of errors!

Read the passage in box A and try to understand it. Then rewrite it in box B on the next page without spelling, grammatical or punctuation errors. Compare your finished work with the suggested version on page 87.

Box A

Anyone desirable to write books or reports, be they short or long, should strive too maximise they're optimal use of one's English grammar and obliviously there is an need for correct spelling two one should not neglect punctuation neither.

Frequent lea, many people and individuals become confusing or just do not no it, when righting, when words that mean different, when sounding identically, or when pronounced very similar, are knot too bee spelled inn the same whey. The quay two suck seeding is dew care, a lack off witch Leeds too Miss Spellings that mite otherwise of bean a voided. Spell chequers donut find awl missed takes.

Despite all the pitfalls how ever, with practise, patients and the right altitude, any one can soon become a grate writer and speaker, as what I did.

Box B Now rewrite the passage in the space below without errors.

4 In each of the statements listed in the table below, suggest what the body language described might mean.

Statement	What might this body language mean?
a) You are talking to your manager when he steps away from you and crosses his arms over his chest.	
b) You are talking to your friend about what she did at the weekend but she's avoiding making eye contact with you.	
c) During a tutorial session, your tutor is constantly tapping his fingers on the arm of his chair.	
d) Whenever you talk to your friend about your next assignment she bites her lower lip.	

Improving your maths or numeracy skills

If you think numeracy isn't relevant to you, then think again! Numeracy is an essential life skill. If you can't carry out basic calculations accurately then you will have problems, perhaps when you least expect them. You'll often encounter numbers in various contexts – sometimes they will be correctly given, sometimes not. Unless you have a basic understanding about numeracy, you won't be able to tell the difference.

Good numeracy skills will improve your ability to express yourself, especially in assignments and at work. If you have problems, there are strategies that you can practise to help:

- Do basic calculations in your head, then check them on a calculator.
- Ask your tutor for help if important calculations give you problems.
- When you are using your computer, use the onscreen calculator (or a spreadsheet package) to do calculations.
- Investigate puzzle sites and brain training software, such as Dr Kageyama's Maths Training by Nintendo.

Action points

1 Go to page 88 to find out how to gain access to websites which can help you to improve your numeracy skills.

2 Try the following task with a friend or family member.

Each of you should write down 36 simple calculations in a list, e.g. 8 × 6, 19 – 8, 14 + 6. Exchange lists. See who can answer the most calculations correctly in the shortest time.

3 Figures aren't always what they appear to be. For example, Sophie watches *Who Wants To Be A Millionaire?* She hears Chris Tarrant say that there have been over 500 shows, with 1200 contestants who have each won over £50,000 on average. Five people have won £1 million.

Sophie says she is going to enter because she is almost certain to win more than £50,000 and could even win a million pounds.

a) On the figures given, what is the approximate total of money won over 500 shows (to the nearest £ million)?

b) Assuming that Sophie is chosen to appear on the show, and makes it on air as a contestant, do you think Sophie's argument that she will 'almost certainly' win more than £50,000 is correct? Give a reason for your answer. (The correct answer is on page 88.)

4 You have a part-time job and have been asked to carry out a survey on the usage of the drinks vending machine. Of the 500 people surveyed:
- 225 use the machine to buy one cup of coffee only
- 100 use the machine to buy one cup of tea only
- 75 use the machine to buy one cup of cold drinks only
- 50 use the machine to buy one cup of hot chocolate only
- the rest are non-users
- the ratio of male to female users is 2:1.

a) How many men in your survey use the machine?

b) How many women in your survey use the machine?

c) Calculate the proportion of the people in your survey that use the machine. Express this as a fraction and a percentage.

d) What is the ratio of coffee drinkers to tea drinkers in your survey?

e) What is the ratio of coffee drinkers to hot chocolate drinkers in your survey?

f) If people continue to purchase from the machine in the same ratio found in your survey, and last month 1800 cups of coffee were sold, what would you expect the sales of the cold drinks to be?

g) Using the answer to f), if coffee costs 65p and all cold drinks cost 60p, how much would have been spent in total last month on these two items?

Improving your ICT skills

Good ICT skills are an asset in many aspects of your daily life and not just for those studying to be IT practitioners.

The following are ways in which you can Improve your ICT skills:

- Check that you can use the main features of the software packages you need to produce your assignments, eg Word, Excel and PowerPoint.
- Choose a good search engine and learn to use it properly. For more information, go to page 88.
- Developing and using your IT skills enables you to enhance your assignments. This may include learning how to import and export text and artwork from one package to another; taking digital photographs and inserting them into your work and/or creating drawings or diagrams by using appropriate software.

Action points

1 Check your basic knowledge of IT terminology by identifying each of these items on your computer screen:

a) taskbar	**f)** scroll bars
b) toolbar	**g)** status bar
c) title bar	**h)** insertion point
d) menu bar	**i)** maximise/
e) mouse pointer	minimise button.

2 Assess your IT skills by identifying the packages and operations you find easy to use and those that you find more difficult. If you use Microsoft Office products (Word, PowerPoint, Access or Excel) you can find out more about improving your skills online. Go to page 88 to find out how to access a useful website.

3 Search the internet to find a useful dictionary of IT terms. Bookmark it for future use. Find out the meaning of any of the following terms that you don't know already:

a) portal

b) cached link

c) home page

d) browser

e) firewall

f) HTML

g) URL

h) cookie

i) hyperlink

j) freeware.

Proofreading and document preparation skills

Improving your keyboard, document production and general IT skills can save you hours of time. When you have good skills, the work you produce will be of a far more professional standard.

- Think about learning to touch type. Your centre may have a workshop you can join, or you can use an online program – go to page 88 to find out how you can access websites that will allow you to test and work on improving your typing skills.

- Obtain correct examples of any document formats you will have to use, such as a report or summary, either from your tutor, the internet or from a textbook.

- Proofread all your work carefully. A spellchecker won't find all your mistakes, so you must read through it yourself as well.

- Make sure your work looks professional by using a suitable typeface and font size, as well as reasonable margins.

- Print your work and store the printouts neatly, so that it stays in perfect condition for when you hand it in.

Action points

1 You can check and improve your typing skills using online typing sites – see link in previous section.

2 Check your ability to create documents by scoring yourself out of 5 for each of the following questions, where 5 is something you can do easily and 0 is something you can't do at all. Then focus on improving every score where you rated yourself 3 or less.

I know how to:

a) create a new document and open a saved document _____

b) use the mouse to click, double-click and drag objects _____

c) use drop-down menus _____

d) customise my toolbars by adding or deleting options _____

e) save and/or print a document _____

f) create folders and sub-folders to organise my work _____

g) move a folder I use regularly to My Places _____

h) amend text in a document _____

i) select, copy, paste and delete information in a document _____

j) quickly find and replace text in a document _____

k) insert special characters _____

l) create a table or insert a diagram in a document _____

m) change the text size, font and colour _____

n) add bold, italics or underscore _____

o) create a bullet or numbered list _____

p) align text left, right or centred _____

q) format pages before they are printed _____

r) proofread a document so that there are no mistakes _____.

Answers

Activity: Let's give you a tip... (page 64)

a) i) Fact
ii) Opinion – the number cannot be validated
iii) Fact
iv) Opinion
v) Opinion
vi) Opinion – again the number is estimated

Skills building answers

PLTS Action points (page 77)

1 a) Use your time wisely = **5** Self-managers
b) Understand how to research and analyse information = **1** Independent enquirers, **5** Self-managers
c) Work productively as a member of a group = **4** Team workers, **6** Effective participators
d) Understand yourself = **3** Reflective learners
e) Utilise all your resources = **5** Self-managers
f) Maximise your opportunities and manage your problems = **1** Independent enquirers, **2** Creative thinkers, **3** Reflective learners, **5** Self-managers

2 a) Factors to consider in relation to the increased photocopying/printing charges include: the comparative prices charged by other schools/colleges, how often there is a price rise, whether any printing or photocopying at all can be done without charge, whether there are any concessions for special tasks or assignments, the availability of class sets of books/popular library books for loan (which reduces the need for photocopying.)

b) i) An earlier start will be more likely to negatively affect those who live further away and who are reliant on public transport, particularly in rural areas. The earlier finish will benefit anyone who has a part-time job that starts on a Friday afternoon or who has after college commitments, such as looking after younger sisters or brothers.

ii) The scope for compromise would depend on whether there are any classes between 11 am and 2 pm on a Friday, whether tutors had any flexibility and whether the new 9 am – 11 am class could be moved to another time or day.

c) One strategy would be to allow discussion for a set time, ensure everyone had spoken, then put the issue to a vote. The leader should prompt suggestions from quieter members by asking people individually what they think.

Literacy skills action points (page 81)

2 a) The statement reads as if it is acceptable to either charge it or dispose of it in fire.
b) Do not connect this battery improperly. Do not recharge it and do not dispose of it in fire.

3 Anyone who wishes to write books or reports, whether short or long, should try to use English grammatically. Obviously there is a need for correct spelling, too. Punctuation should also not be neglected.

Frequently, people confuse words with different meanings when they are writing, especially when these sound identical or very similar, even when they must not be spelled in the same way. The key to succeeding is due care, a lack of which leads to misspellings that might otherwise have been avoided. Spellcheckers do not find all mistakes.

Despite all the pitfalls, however, with practice, patience and the right attitude, anyone can soon become a great writer and speaker, like me.

4 Possible answers

a) Stepping backwards and crossing arms across the chest might indicate that your manager is creating a barrier between you and himself, or that he is angry.

b) Your friend might be feeling guilty about what she did at the weekend or not confident that you will approve of what she tells you.

c) Your tutor might be frustrated as he has many things to do and so wants the tutorial to be over quickly.

d) Your friend might be anxious about the next assignment or about the time she has to complete it.

Numeracy action points (page 84)

3 a) £60 million

b) Sophie's argument is incorrect as £50,000 is an average, i.e. some contestants will win more, but many will win much less. The distribution of prizes is greater at lower amounts because more people win small amounts of money than large amounts – and only five have won the top prize of £1 million.

4 a) 300

b) 150

c) 9/10ths, 90%

d) 225:100 (= 45:20) = 9:4

e) 225:50 = 9:2

f) 600

g) £1530

Accessing website links

Links to various websites are referred to throughout this BTEC Level 3 National Study Skills Guide. To ensure that these links are up-to-date, that they work and that the sites aren't inadvertently linked to any material that could be considered offensive, we have made the links available on our website: www.pearsonhotlinks.co.uk. When you visit the site, search for either the title BTEC Level 3 National Study Skills Guide in Health and Social Care or ISBN 9781846905582. From here you can gain access to the website links and information on how they can be used to help you with your studies.

Useful terms

Accreditation of Prior Learning (APL)
Some of your previous achievements and experiences may be able to be used to count towards your qualification.

Apprenticeships
Schemes that enable you to work and earn money at the same time as you gain further qualifications (an NVQ award and a technical certificate) and improve your functional skills. Apprentices learn work-based skills relevant to their job role and their chosen industry. Go to page 88 to see how to access a useful website where you can find out more.

Assessment methods
Techniques used to check that your work demonstrates the learning and understanding required for your qualification, such as assignments, case studies and practical tasks.

Assessor
An assessor is the tutor who marks or assesses your work.

Assignment
A complex task or mini-project set to meet specific grading criteria and learning outcomes.

Awarding body
An organisation responsible for devising, assessing and issuing qualifications. The awarding body for all BTEC qualifications is Edexcel.

Credit value
The number of credits attached to your BTEC course. The credit value increases in relation to the length of time you need to complete the course, from 30 credits for a BTEC Level 3 Certificate, 60 credits for a Subsidiary Diploma, 120 credits for a Diploma, up to 180 credits for an Extended Diploma.

Degrees
Higher education qualifications offered by universities and colleges. Foundation degrees take two years to complete; honours degrees may take three years or longer.

Department for Business Innovation and Skills (BIS)
BIS is responsible for further and higher education and skills training, as well as functions related to trade and industry. See page 88 for information on how to access a website where you can find out more.

Department for Education
The Department for Education is the government department responsible for schools and education, as well as for children's services. See page 88 for information on how to access a website where you can find out more.

Distance learning
When you learn and/or study for a qualification at home or at work. You communicate with your tutor and/or the centre that organises the course by post, telephone or electronically.

Educational Maintenance Award (EMA)
An EMA is a means-tested award that provides eligible learners under 19, who are studying a full-time course at school or college, with a cash sum of money every week. Go to page 88 to see how to access a useful website where you can find out more.

External verification
Formal checking of the programme by an Edexcel representative that focuses on sampling various assignments to check content, accurate assessment and grading.

Forbidden combinations
There are some qualifications that cannot be taken simultaneously because their content is too similar.

Functional skills
Practical skills in English, maths and ICT that enable people to work confidently, effectively and independently. Level 2 Functional Skills are mapped to the units of BTEC Level 3 National qualifications. They aren't compulsory to achieve on the course, but are of great use.

Grade boundaries
Pre-set points that determine whether you will achieve a pass, merit or distinction as the overall final grade(s) for your qualification.

Grading criteria
The specific evidence you have to demonstrate to obtain a particular grade in the unit.

Grading domains
The main areas of learning that support the learning outcomes. On a BTEC Level 3 National course these are: application of knowledge and understanding; development of practical and technical skills; personal development for occupational roles; application of PLTS and functional skills.

Grading grid
The table in each unit of your qualification specification that sets out what you have to show you can do.

Higher education (HE)
Post-secondary and post-further education, usually provided by universities and colleges.

Higher-level skills
These are skills such as evaluating or critically assessing information. They are more difficult than lower-level skills such as writing a description or making a list. You must be able to demonstrate higher-level skills to achieve a distinction.

Indicative reading
Recommended books and journals whose content is both suitable and relevant for the BTEC unit studied.

Induction
A short programme of events at the start of a course designed to give you essential information, and introduce you to your fellow learners and tutors, so that you can settle down as quickly and easily as possible.

Internal verification
The quality checks carried out by nominated tutors at your school or college to ensure that all assignments are at the right level, cover appropriate learning outcomes and grading criteria, and that all assessors are marking work consistently and to the same standard.

Investors in People (IiP)
A national quality standard that sets a level of good practice for training and developing of people within a business. Participating organisations must demonstrate commitment to achieve the standard.

Learning outcomes
The knowledge and skills you must demonstrate to show that you have effectively learned a unit.

Learning support
Additional help that is available to all learners in a school or college who have learning difficulties or other special needs.

Levels of study
The depth, breadth and complexity of knowledge, understanding and skills required to achieve a qualification, which also determines its level. Level 2 equates to GCSE level and Level 3 equates to A-level. As you successfully achieve one level, you can then progress to the next. BTEC qualifications are offered at Entry Level, then Levels 1, 2, 3, 4 and 5.

Local Education Authority (LEA)
The local government body responsible for providing education for all learners of compulsory school age. The LEA is also responsible for managing the education budget for 16–19 learners in its area.

Mandatory units
These are units that all learners must complete to gain a qualification; in this case a BTEC Level 3 National. Some BTEC qualifications have an over-arching title, eg Construction, but within Construction you can choose different pathways. Your chosen pathway may have additional mandatory units specific to that pathway.

Mentor
A more experienced person who will guide you, and counsel you if you have a problem or difficulty.

Mode of delivery
The way in which a qualification is offered to learners for example, part-time, full-time, as a short course or by distance learning.

National Occupational Standard (NOS)
Statements of the skills, knowledge and understanding you need to develop in order to be competent at a particular job.

National Vocational Qualification (NVQ)
Qualifications that concentrate on the practical skills and knowledge required to do a job competently. They are usually assessed in the workplace and range from Level 1 (the lowest) to Level 5 (the highest).

Nested qualifications
Qualifications that have 'common' units, so that learners can easily progress from one to another by adding on more units

Ofqual
The public body responsible for regulating qualifications, exams and tests in England.

Optional units
Units on your course from which you may be able to make a choice. They help you specialise your skills, knowledge and understanding and may help progression into work or further education.

Pathway
All BTEC Level 3 National qualifications comprise a small number of mandatory units and a larger number of optional units. These units are grouped into different combinations to provide alternative pathways to achieving the qualification. These pathways are usually linked to different career preferences.

Peer review
This involves feedback on your performance by your peers (members of your team, or class group.) You will also be given an opportunity to review their performance.

Plagiarism
The practice of copying someone else's work, or work from any other sources (eg the internet), and passing it off as your own. This practice is strictly forbidden on all courses.

Personal, learning and thinking skills (PLTS)
The skills, personal qualities and behaviour that improve your ability to work independently. Developing these skills makes you more effective and confident at work. Opportunities for developing these skills are a feature of all BTEC Level 3 National courses. These skills aren't compulsory to achieve on the course, but are of great use to you.

Portfolio
A collection of work compiled by a learner, usually as evidence of learning, to present to an assessor.

Procrastinator
Someone who is forever putting off or delaying work, either because they are lazy or because they have poor organisational skills.

Professional body
An organisation that exists to promote or support a particular profession; for example, the Royal Institute of British Architects (RIBA).

Professional development and training
This involves undertaking activities relevant to your job to increase and/or update your knowledge and skills.

Project
A project is a comprehensive piece of work, which normally involves original research and investigation by an individual or by a team. The findings and results may be presented in writing and summarised as a presentation.

Qualifications and Credit Framework (QCF)
The QCF is a framework for recognising skills and qualifications. It does this by awarding credit for qualifications and units so that they are easier to measure and compare. All BTEC Level 3 National qualifications are part of the QCF.

Qualifications and Curriculum Development Agency (QCDA)
The QCDA is responsible for maintaining and developing the national curriculum, delivering assessments, tests and examinations and reforming qualifications.

Quality assurance
In education, this is the process of continually checking that a course of study is meeting the specific requirements set down by the awarding body.

Sector Skills Councils (SSCs)
The 25 employer-led, independent organisations responsible for improving workforce skills in the UK by identifying skill gaps and improving learning in the workplace. Each council covers a different type of industry.

Semester
Many universities and colleges divide their academic year into two halves or semesters, one from September to January and one from February to July.

Seminar

A learning event involving a group of learners and a tutor, which may be learner-led, and follow research into a topic that has been introduced at an earlier stage.

Study buddy

A person in your group or class who takes notes for you and keeps you informed of important developments if you are absent. You do the same for them in return.

Time-constrained assignment

An assessment you must complete within a fixed time limit.

Tutorial

An individual or small group meeting with your tutor at which you can discuss your current work and other more general course issues. At an individual tutorial, your progress on the course will be discussed and you can raise any concerns or personal worries you may have.

The University and Colleges Admissions Service (UCAS)

UCAS (pronounced 'you-cass') is the central organisation that processes all applications for higher education (HE) courses.

UCAS points

The number of points allocated by UCAS for the qualifications you have obtained. Higher education institutions specify how many points you need to be accepted on the courses they offer. See page 88 for information on how to access the UCAS website where you can find out more.

Unit abstract

The summary at the start of each BTEC unit that tells you what the unit is about.

Unit content

Details about the topics covered by the unit and the knowledge and skills you need to complete it.

Unit points

The number of points you gain when you complete a unit. These will depend on the grade you achieve (pass, merit or distinction).

Vocational qualification

Designed to develop knowledge and understanding relevant to a chosen area of work.

Work experience

Time you spend on an employer's premises when you learn about the enterprise, carry out work-based tasks and develop skills and knowledge.

Please note that all information given within these useful terms was correct at the time of going to print.